C000177607

THE CON
EUROPE͟   ͟͟͟ ͟ ͟   ͟͟͟
AND
AMPHIBIANS

Edited by

Keith Corbett

on behalf of

The Conservation Committee of the
Societas Europaea Herpetologica

*also serving as the IUCN/SSC European
Reptile and Amphibian Specialist Group*

CHRISTOPHER HELM
London

© 1989 Keith Corbett
Christopher Helm (Publishers) Ltd, Imperial House
21-25 North Street, Bromley, Kent BR1 1SD

ISBN 0-7470-0413-7

A CIP catalogue record for this book
is available from the British Library

COUNCIL OF EUROPE CONSEIL DE L'EUROPE

WWF

Camera-ready copy produced by
The Nature Conservation Bureau, Thatcham, Berks.

Printed and bound in Great Britain by
Billings and Sons, Ltd, Worcester

Contents

Page

Foreword and Acknowledgements
List of Abbreviations Used

**Part One   Background to Europe's Reptiles
and Amphibians**

Checklist of Species   3

1   Introduction   11

Numbers and Distribution of Species   11
Habitats   12
Threats   14
International Law   17

2   Priority Species for Conservation Action   24

**Part Two   Review of Species and Habitat
Conservation Priorities**

3   Introduction   31

4   Key Species in the Council of Europe Area   35

Fire-bellied Toad *Bombina bombina*   35
Mallorcan Midwife Toad *Alytes muletensis*   42
Italian Spadefoot *Pelobates fuscus insubricus*   47
Italian Agile Frog *Rana latastei*   52
The Marine Turtles
  Caretta caretta and *Chelonia mydas*   58
Ibiza Wall Lizard *Podarcis pityusensis* and
Lilford's Wall Lizard *Podarcis lilfordi*   74

Page

Orsini's Viper *Vipera ursinii ursinii* 79
Meadow Viper *Vipera (ursinii) rakosiensis* 84
Milos Viper *Vipera schweizeri* and
Milos Wall Lizard *Podarcis milensis milensis* 90

5 **Critical Species Assemblages
in the Council of Europe Area** 102

East Sardinia (Italy) 102
Evros (Greece) 112

6 **Further Work Required on
Critical Species and Species Assemblages** 121

Part Three Country Accounts

7 **Introduction** 127
8 **Denmark** 129
9 **Norway** 135
10 **Sweden** 138
11 **Finland** 145
12 **Poland** 147
13 **Czechoslovakia** 150
14 **Democratic Republic of Germany** 153
15 **Federal Republic of Germany** 159
16 **Netherlands** 167
17 **Belgium** 173
18 **Luxembourg** 179
19 **United Kingdom** 183
Great Britain 183
Jersey 190
Northern Ireland 193
20 **Eire** 194

Table of Contents

                                                                    Page

21   **Portugal**   197

22   **Spain**   200

23   **France**   206

24   **Monaco**   212

25   **Switzerland**   214

26   **Liechtenstein**   219

27   **Italy**   220

28   **Malta**   227

29   **Austria**   230

30   **Hungary**   235

31   **Yugoslavia**   239

32   **Romania**   243

33   **Bulgaria**   247

34   **Greece**   250

35   **Turkey**   254

36   **Cyprus**   259

Appendices

I   Recommendation 13 (1988) of the
      Standing Committee of the Berne Convention   262

II   Resolution 22 (1978) of the Committee of
      Ministers of the Council of Europe   266

III   Recommendation 7 (1987) of the
      Standing Committee of the Berne Convention   269

IV   Recommendation 9 (1987) of the
      Standing Committee of the Berne Convention   271

V   Recommendation 8 (1987) of the
      Standing Committee of the Berne Convention   273

Foreword
and
Acknowledgements

This book and the conservation strategy embodied within it has been
written by a number of the members of the Conservation Committee of the Societas Europaea Herpetologica. Those readers who
have had experience of drafting by committee will realise the
numerous problems that such an exercise entails. Our job was
further compounded by language and translation difficulties on top
of a tight deadline for publication. If we were to start again with the
luxuries of hindsight and more time, this book would surely have
read rather differently. However, the essential facts about the status
of reptiles and amphibians in Europe and their conservation
requirements at national and international levels would remain
intact.

The principal contributors to this book were:

Claes Andren (Sweden), lecturer in zoology at the University of
Göteborg where he carries out research on vipers of Europe and
West Asia, and responsible to the Swedish Nature Conservation
Board for conservation and research on threatened reptiles and
amphibians.

Emilio Balletto (Italy), professor of zoology at Turin University
where he conducts research into the taxonomy and distribution of
green frogs in Europe.

Keith Corbett (United Kingdom), Conservation Officer of the

Herpetological Conservation Trust and Chair of the SEH Conservation Committee since its establishment in 1981. He carries out research on the ecology, distribution and conservation of *Lacerta agilis* in the UK and is involved in the conservation of marine turtles in the Mediterranean.

Brian Groombridge (United Kingdom), Senior Research Officer and Red Data List compiler at the World Conservation Monitoring Centre of IUCN/WWF/UNEP, and undertakes research into the herpetofauna of Indian rainforests and marine turtles of the Indian Ocean.

Kurt Grossenbacher (Switzerland) Curator of Herpetology at the Berne Musueum of Natural History and head of the Swiss Coordination Centre for the protection of amphibians and reptiles. He studies amphibian larval development in the Alps as well as the distribution of the Swiss herpetofauna and is involved with the conservation of European amphibians.

Rene Honegger (Switzerland) Curator of Herpetology at Zurich Zoo and is involved in the implementation of the Convention on International Trade in Endangered Species. He compiled the first Red Data Book on amphibians and reptiles and initiated the involvement of the Council of Europe in herpetofauna conservation.

Richard Podloucky (West Germany) herpetological officer for the Lower Saxony Department of Nature Conservation and Landscape Management and carries out field research on the distribution, protection and management of amphibians and reptiles and has worked on tortoises and terrapins in both Europe and South America.

Anton Stumpel (Netherlands) an ecologist at the State Research Institute for Nature Conservation and Landscape Management. He does applied research in plant and animal ecology including work on threatened herpetofauna with particular emphasis on the ecology of *Hyla arborea* in northern Europe.

In addition, we are most grateful to all those who directly contributed and updated information for this book, many of whom are also members of the SEH Conservation Committee (asterisked): A.

Bea*, D. Dolman*, K. Fog, H. Grillitsch*, Z. Korsos*, V. Lanka*, J. Lescure*, A. Martinez-Rica*, G. van Mook, G. Nilson, A. Nollert, P. Scholte, D. Stubbs, S. Stumpel, J. Terhivuo.

A number of people kindly provided valuable additional material: J. Alcover, E. Arnold, J.-P. Baron, T. Beebee, V. Beshkov, D. Bird, H. Bringsoe, A. Cooke, J. Crespo, I. Darevsky, A. Demetropoulos, E. Fernandez-Galiano, K. Fritz, R. Geldiay, M. Grischwitz, M. Janisch, M. Kasparek, K. Klemmer, T. Langton, B. Lanza, A. Machado, J. Mayol, G. Nechay, J. Pickett, M. Speight, J. Sultana, Z. Takacs, L. Venizelos, E. Weiderkinch and the UK Customs and Excise Service.

The World Wide Fund for Nature (WWF-International) generously provided financial support for some of the field studies. Simon Stuart of the IUCN Species Survival Commission has been tireless in his pursuit of this work from its inception and we are indebted for his continual effort and input. Paul Goriup, Sue Everett and John Norton of the Nature Conservation Bureau did a sterling job of turning the scruffy manuscripts into printable copy.

Our final word of thanks goes to Veit Koester who, as Chair of the Standing Committee of the Berne Convention, has patiently supported our work and the cause of reptile and amphibian conservation by smoothing the passage of the various Recommendations adopted by the contracting parties, and to members of the Secretariat of the Council of Europe, particularly P. Baum and J.-P. Ribaut, who brought the critical habitat project into being and kindly permitted the results to be included in this book.

List of Abbreviations Used in the Text

CITES	Washington Convention on International Trade in Endangered Species of Fauna and Flora, 1975
CoE	Council of Europe
EEC	European Economic Community
IUCN	International Union for Conservation of Nature and Natural Resources
SEH	Societas Europaea Herpetologica
SSC	Species Survival Commission of IUCN
SSSI	Site of Special Scientific Interest
Unesco	United Nations Educational, Scientific and Cultural Organisation
SOPTOM	Station d'Observation et de protection des Tortues des Maures
UNEP	United Nations Environment Programme
WWF	World Wide Fund for Nature (formerly World Wildlife Fund)

Part One

Background to Europe's Reptiles and Amphibians

Checklist of Reptiles and Amphibians Indigenous to Europe, including Turkey, Cyprus and the western Soviet Union

Taxa shown with an asterisk are listed in Appendix II of the Berne Protection and therefore merit strict protection within the Council of Europe area and Finland.

Amphibians

Alytes cistemasii *	Iberian midwife toad
Alytes muletensis *	Mallorcan midwife toad
Alytes obstetricans *	Midwife toad
Bombina bombina *	Fire-bellied toad
Bombina variegata *	Yellow-bellied toad
Bufo bufo	Common toad
Bufo calamita *	Natterjack toad
Bufo viridis *	Green toad, variegated toad
Chioglossa lusitanica *	Gold-striped salamander
Discoglossus galganoi *	
Discoglossus jeanneae *	
Discoglossus montalentii	
Discoglossus pictus *	Painted frog
Discoglossus sardus *	Tyrrhenian painted frog
Euproctus asper *	Pyrenean brook salamander, Pyrenean mountain newt
Euproctus montanus *	Pyrenean mountain newt
Euproctus platycephalus *	Sardinian brook salamander
Speleomantes ambrosii *	
Speleomantes flavus *	Monte Albo cave salamander
Speleomantes genei *	Sardinian cave salamander
Speleomantes imperialis *	
Speleomantes italicus *	Italian cave salamander
Speleomantes supramontis *	Supramonte cave salamander

Hyla arborea*	European tree frog, green tree frog, common tree frog
Hyla meridionalis*	Mediterranean tree frog, stripeless tree frog
Hyla sarda*	Sardinian tree frog, Tyrrhenian tree frog
Hyla savignyi	Savignyi's tree frog, yellow-lemon tree frog
Mertensiella caucasica	Caucasian salamander
Mertensiella luschani*	Lycian salamander, Luschan's salamander
Neurergus crocatus	Azerbaijan newt
Neurergus strauchii	
Pelobates cultripes*	Iberian spadefoot, western spadefoot
Pelobates fuscus*	Common spadefoot, western spadefoot
Pelobates fuscus insubricus*	Italian spadefoot
Pelobates syriacus*	Eastern spadefoot, Syrian spadefoot
Pelodytes caucasicus*	Caucasian parsley frog
Pelodytes punctatus	Parsley frog, spotted mud frog
Pleurodeles waltl	Spanish newt, ribbed newt, sharp-ribbed salamander, Iberian newt
Proteus anguinus*	Olm, blind salamander
Rana arvalis*	Moor frog, field frog
Rana camerani	
Rana catesbiana	
Rana dalmatina*	Agile frog, leap frog
Rana epeirotica	Epeirus frog
Rana kl. esculenta	Edible frog, green frog
Rana graeca	Greek stream frog
Rana holtzi	
Rana iberica*	Spanish frog, Iberian frog
Rana italica*	Italian stream frog
Rana latastei*	Italian (agile) frog, Lataste's frog
Rana lessonae	Pool frog, little waterfrog
Rana macrocnemis	Caucasian frog, Iranian long-legged frog
Rana perezi	Iberian waterfrog, Perez's frog
Rana ridibunda	Lake frog, marsh frog
Rana shquiperica	Balkan frog
Rana temporaria	Grass frog, common frog
Salamandra atra*	Alpine salamander, black salamander
Salamandra (atra) aurorae	Golden salamander

Salamandra corsica	Corsican salamander
Salamandra salamandra	Fire salamander, spotted salamander, European salamander
Salamandrella keyserlingii	Siberian salamander
*Salamandrina terdigitata**	Spectacled salamander
Triturus alpestris	Alpine newt
Triturus boscai	Bosca's newt
*Triturus carnifex**	Alpine crested newt, Italian warty newt
*Triturus cristatus**	Crested newt, warty newt
*Triturus dobrogicus**	Danube crested newt
Triturus helveticus	Palmate newt
*Triturus italicus**	Italian newt
*Triturus karelini**	Balkan crested newt
Triturus marmoratus	Marbled newt
*Triturus montandoni**	Montandon's newt, Carpathian newt
Triturus vittatus	Banded newt
Triturus vulgaris	Smooth newt, Common newt, eft

Reptiles

Ablepharus bivittatus	
*Ablepharus kitaibelii**	Balkan skink, snake-eyed skink, European copper skink
Acanthodactylus boskianus	Bosc's sandracer, Bosc's fringe-toed lizard
Acanthodactylus erythrurus	Spiny-footed lizard
Agkistrodon halys	Halys viper
*Algyroides fitzingeri**	Pygmy algyroides
*Algyroides marchi**	Spanish algyroides, Spanish lizard
*Algyroides moreoticus**	Greek algyroides
*Algyroides nigropunctatus**	Dalmatian algyroides
Alsophylax pipiens	Caspian straight-fingered gecko
Anguis fragilis	Slow worm, blind worm
Asaccus elisae	
Blanus cinereus	Amphisbaenian
Blanus strauchi	Ringed amphisbaenian
*Caretta caretta**	Loggerhead turtle, common loggerhead
*Chalcides bedriagai**	Bedriaga's skink
Chalcides chalcides	Three-toed skink
*Chalcides occidentalis**	Multiscaled skink
*Chalcides ocellatus**	Eyed skink
Chalcides pistaciae	

*Chalcides sexlineatus**	Six-lined skink
*Chalcides viridanus**	Green skink
*Chamaeleo chamaeleon**	Common chameleon, European chameleon, Mediterranean chameleon
*Chelonia mydas**	Green turtle, edible turtle
Coluber algirus	Algerian whip snake
Coluber caspius	Large whip snake
Coluber cypriensis	
*Coluber hippocrepis**	Horseshoe whip snake
*Coluber jugularis**	Caspian whip snake, green whip snake, Persian large whip snake
*Coluber laurenti**	Balkan whip snake
*Coluber najadum**	Dahl's whip snake
Coluber nummifer	Reuss' whip snake
Coluber ravergieri	Coin-marked snake, Ravergier's whip snake
Coluber rubriceps	Red-headed whip snake
Coluber schmidti	Schmidt's whip snake
Coluber ventromaculatus	
*Coluber viridiflavus**	Western whip snake, European whip snake
*Coronella austriaca**	Smooth snake
Coronella girondica	Bordeaux snake, southern smooth snake
Cyrtopodion basoglui	
Cyrtopodion caspius	Caspian gecko
Cyrtopodion heterocercus	
*Cyrtopodion kotschyi**	Crimean gecko, Kotschy's gecko
Cyrtopodion russowii	Caucasian gecko
Cyrtopodion scaber	
*Dermochelys coriacea** +	Leatherback, leathery turtle, luth
Eirenis barani	
Eirenis collaris	Collared dwarf snake
Eirenis coronella	Crowned peace snake
Eirenis decemlineata	Ten-lined peace snake
Eirenis eiselti	
Eirenis lineomaculata	Spotted line snake
Eirenis modesta	Ring-headed dwarf snake
Eirenis punctatolineata	Dotted dwarf snake
Eirenis rothii	Roth's snake
Elaphe dione	Dione snake
Elaphe hohenackeri	Caucasian snake
*Elaphe longissima**	Aesculapian snake
Elaphe persica	

Checklist of Reptiles and Amphibians

*Elaphe quatuorlineata**	Four-lined snake, four-lined rat snake
Elaphe scalaris	Ladder snake
*Elaphe situla**	Leopard snake
*Emys orbicularis**	European pond terrapin
Eremias arguta	Stepperunner, Motley lizard
Eremias pleskei	Pleske's racerunner
Eremias strauchi	Strauch's racerunner
Eremias suphani	
Eremias velox	Racerunner
*Eretmochelys imbricata** +	Hawksbill turtle
Eryx jaculus	Turkish sand boa, javelin sand boa
Eryx miliaris	Dwarf sand boa
Eumeces schneideri	Schneider's skink
Gallotia atlantica	Atlantic lizard
*Gallotia galloti**	Canary Islands lizard
*Gallotia simonyi**	Hierro giant lizard, Simony's lizard
*Gallotia stehlini**	Stehlin's lizard
Hemidactylus turcicus	Turkish gecko
*Lacerta agilis**	Sand lizard
Lacerta anatolica	Anatolian lizard
Lacerta armeniaca	Armenian lizard
*Lacerta bedriagae**	Bedriaga's rock lizard
Lacerta bithynica	
Lacerta brandti	Persian lizard
Lacerta cappadocica	Cappadocian lizard
Lacerta caucasica	Caucasian lizard
Lacerta chlorogaster	Green-bellied lizard
Lacerta clarkorum	
Lacerta dahli	Dahl's lizard
Lacerta danfordi	Danford's lizard
Lacerta derjugini	Derjugin's lizard
Lacerta dugesii	
*Lacerta graeca**	Greek rock lizard
*Lacerta horvathi**	Horvath's rock lizard
Lacerta laevis	Swift lizard
*Lacerta lepida**	Eyed lizard
Lacerta media	
Lacerta mehelyi	
Lacerta mixta	
*Lacerta monticola**	Iberian rock lizard, Iberian mountain lizard
Lacerta mosorensis	Mosor rock lizard
Lacerta oertzeni	

Lacerta oxycephala	Sharp-snouted rock lizard
Lacerta pamphylica	
*Lacerta parva**	Dwarf lizard
Lacerta parvula	Red-bellied lizard
Lacerta portschinskii	
Lacerta praticola	Pontic lizard, meadow lizard
*Lacerta princeps**	Zagros lizard
Lacerta raddei	Radde's lizard
Lacerta rostombekovi	
Lacerta rudis	Spiny-tailed lizard
Lacerta saxicola	Rock lizard
*Lacerta schreiberi**	Schreiber's (green) lizard
Lacerta strigata	Caspian green lizard
*Lacerta trilineata**	Giant green lizard, Balkan green lizard, three-lined emerald lizard
Lacerta unisexualis	
Lacerta uzzelli	Uzzell's rock lizard
Lacerta valentini	Valentin's rock lizard
*Lacerta viridis**	Green lizard, emerald lizard
Lacerta vivipara	Viviparous lizard, common lizard
*Lepidochelys kempii**	Kemp's ridley, Atlantic ridley
Leptotyphlops macrorhynchus	Worm snake, beaked thread snake
Lytorhynchus diadema	Clifford's snake
Mabuya aurata	Golden grass snake
Mabuya vittata	Bridled skink
Macroprotodon cucullatus	False smooth snake, hooded snake
Malpolon monspessulanus	Montpellier snake
*Mauremys caspica**	Caspian terrapin, stripe-necked terrapin
Mauremys leprosa	Spanish terrapin, leprous terrapin
Megalochilus mystaceus	Toad-headed agama
Natrix maura	Viperine snake
Natrix megalocephala	
Natrix natrix	Grass snake, ringed snake
Natrix natrix corsa	Corsican grass snake
Natrix natrix cetti	Sardinian grass snake
*Natrix tessellata**	Dice snake, tesselated (water) snake
*Ophiomorus punctatissimus**	Speckled snake skink, Greek legless skink, spotted skink
*Ophisaurus apodus**	(European) glass lizard, glass snake
*Ophisops elegans**	Snake-eyed lizard
Phrynocephalus guttatus	Spotted toad-headed agama
Phrynocephalus helioscopus	Sunwatcher
*Phyllodactylus europeaus**	European leaf-fingered gecko

8

Table 1: Numbers of amphibians and reptiles in Europe.		
	Amphibians	Reptiles
Northern region		
Finland	5	5
Norway	5	5
Denmark	14	5
Sweden	13	6
Poland	18	9
Netherlands	16	7
Belgium	17	7
* Eire	3	1
* Great Britain	6	6
* Channel Islands	3	4
Central region		
East Germany	19	8
West Germany	20	12
Czechoslovakia	19	12
Hungary	17	15
Austria	20	14
Switzerland	18	14
Luxembourg	15	7
Southern region		
Portugal	17	28
Spain	24	42
France	27	28
Italy	27	35
Yugoslavia	23	41
Greece	15	51
Romania	19	25
Bulgaria	17	33
Turkey	18	104
* Cyprus	7	24
* Sardinia	8	18
* Corsica	7	11
* Malta	1	9
* Balearic Islands	3	11
* Canary Islands	2	12

*Island(s)

Threats

Like most European wildlife, reptiles and amphibians are at risk from habitat loss and change; but many species are further vulnerable because of their basic biology as well as from human prejudice. Ecologically, most have comparatively small home ranges, in which they are relatively sedentary; they are usually poor colonisers, particularly in cooler climates, and are often reliant on a brief immature phase for any potential spread. With the exception of the fixed route breeding migrations of some amphibians and natricine snakes, and of the marine turtles, amphibians and reptiles generally exhibit very limited abilities and little instinct for movement over long distances or for dispersal over a large area or region. They therefore have very little scope to avoid even temporary threats or adverse changes to their habitats. Yet it is a widely held misconception, even among naturalists and conservationists, that amphibians and reptiles somehow move out as needs dictate, perhaps to return when conditions improve. In fact this depends on adjacent breeding populations and is more often than not the underlying cause of continuing declines and local extinctions. It should go without saying that, unlike plants and many invertebrates, they do not have any resting, seed, or spore phases to tide them over these rapid man-made changes; nor like birds and many invertebrates do they have any powers of flight to facilitate escape and subsequent return.

Put succinctly, the reptiles and amphibians are generally unable to cope with the speed of today's man-made changes. This natural vulnerability to technological man's exploitation of the countryside and its habitats (Plate 6) is further accentuated by these species' requirements to overwinter in a state of torpor over much of Europe, an hibernation period which may exceed six months in north temperate or montane regions. The list of known causes of decline is long, including: agricultural intensification, overgrazing, afforestation, pollution, water abstraction, drainage (especially of meadows), burning (accidental, or as a deliberate management), road and piste construction, urbanisation, tourist development (especially in coastal and mountain areas) and poisoning

Another underlying problem for reptile and amphibian conservation is the frequent reliance on purely botanical criteria for reserve selection and habitat protection. For it is not the floral composition so much as vegetation structure, together with topographical features that may determine the herpetofaunal value of an area. Conservation management designed to maintain the botanical or landscape interest of a site may be disastrous for reptiles in particular, e.g. insensitively timed meadow cutting, or burning, or inappropriate grazing. A recent unfortunate example comes from the use of an innovative 'Plaagen Machin' peat stripper on the Dutch heathlands. Designed to combat a trend to grass-dominated heaths through unnatural enrichment, economic pressures led to its unfettered use on stands of mature dry heath on nature reserves. Whilst it ensured the survival of the heathers by its top-soil stripping, it produced serious (and predicted) local losses of reptile populations. A similar faunal impoverishment has been caused by excessive cutting of the Danubian meadows in Austria and Hungary, using mechanical means.

Genuine clashes with the perceived conservation needs of other fauna are thankfully infrequent and then usually resolved by site zoning for different uses. However the practice of encouraging wildfowl to ponds and small lakes, or of overstocking them with fish, or of rearing game birds, may all present problems. It is doubtful, though, whether any of these activities could be fairly classified as conserving wildlife or ecosystems.

Persecution includes especially killing of snakes, for whatever reason, and direct poisoning, e.g in the recent campaign against *Lacerta lepida* (Plate 7) on behalf of 'Project Alectoris' (aimed at establishing red-legged partridges *Alectoris rufa* for hunting), and the deliberate poisoning of lizards in the Canary Islands and the Balearic Islands.

This persecution of reptiles and amphibians is due to widespread fear and superstition. This in turn has contributed to their lack of conservation. Also, they generally lack importance as an economic resource, e.g. for hunting, which might have prompted their better safeguard as a natural resource. Their aesthetic appeal, and indeed their presence to the observer, does not match that presented by many birds, butterflies or flowering plants. This in itself is a little unjustified when one considers the undeniable attractiveness of such species as marbled, alpine and banded newts, tree frog, green toad, eyed and sand lizards, slow-worm or sand boa. However, to some, the sight of the latter two species might simply evoke man's instinctive fear of snakes, a major cause of persecution of many quite harmless species. The former groups too are often associated with adverse folk-lore about their poisonous or evil nature, e.g. for toads, salamanders and geckos. Better education and publicity would undoubtedly help, but even with governments directly responsible for their region's or nation's wildlife heritage, these attitudes still persist to influence the administrations. With advancing herpetological knowledge and research, their conservation needs are often addressed slowly if at all; the reader may judge from the various national chapters later in this book.

If herpetologists have not done enough to highlight the decline of amphibian and reptile populations and the causes and remedies, or to improve their public image, then this domestic failing must be greatly worsened by the growing tendency to keep these animals in terraria. Sadly, such fanciers form the majority of the membership of all national and regional herpetological societies in Europe, and although the individual's interest may be entirely benign, the resulting collection and trade pressures on the wild animals can be quite serious. This is the more so as the members may 'progress' towards keeping the rarer and more exotic species. Two recent victims have been the harmless meadow and Caucasian vipers, accelerated along their roads to extinction by this misdirected interest in wildlife.

It is often argued that most amateur herpetologists became interested by their initial catching, or purchase, and keeping of reptiles and amphibians, or that their 'studies' of the habits of these species within indoor tanks and cages lent some scientific justification for their activity. While the former comment is valid, it could and should be confined only to controlled and licensed captive bred stocks, and restricted to species that are known to do well in captivity. The latter view has little credibility or substance, especially when compared to the value and pleasure of observations made in the field. Other forms of unwarranted exploitation involve excessive collections made in the name of research or museum stocks; the deliberate and accidental catching of marine turtles during long-lining and trawling; and the extensive export of green frogs from Romania and Turkey (and Egypt) for the culinary markets of France and Switzerland. This frog trade is causing current concern for its potential ecological impact in the exporting countries, though it is equally the end of initiating detailed surveys. After that comes the essential process of determining priorities; there are never likely to be enough resources to fund adequately a non-economic exercise like reptile conservation, no matter how well deserved.

This book begins at the international level with a comparative rating of species by conservation priority, and follows this in Part Two with species and habitat information gained from projects that were contracted to the SEH by the Council of Europe. The projects were selected to address most of the highest species and habitat conservation priorities. Part Two concludes with recommendations for additional projects that need to be done to complete work on the most endangered species, as well as the richer herpetofaunal associations and critical ecosystems. While these projects represent an international perception of the top conservation priorities in Europe, the proposals within the subsequent national chapters of Part Three comprise the backbone of a more comprehensive strategy for European reptiles and amphibians. Superimposed on and implicit in this programme would be a series of recovery plans designed and implemented to halt the declines of priority species on an international and national scale and to restore their population strength.

2
Priority Species for Conservation Action

Due to the limited resources for conservation and the relatively low interest in the European herpetofauna, it is essential to assess the comparative conservation status of the 300 or so species found in Europe, and to assign conservation priorities accordingly. This was first attempted for most of the Council of Europe area (Figure 1) in 1982 and 1983 and that study has been continually updated, largely to account for taxonomic changes as much as any new information about species status.

The criteria used to assess conservation priorities for the European herpetofauna were:

-       total world range;
-       extent of range and size of population in Europe;
-       whether or not the species is endemic to Europe;
-       rate of recent decline;
-       vulnerability to existing and potential threats;
-       scientific value (ecological, taxonomic, genetic).

The data necessary for this assessment were obtained from herpe-tologists from all over Europe, from literature sources and from some applied research. The species may be classified into one of ten categories, with the most threatened species assigned within categories 1 to 3 (Table 2) and the most widespread, least endangered and commonest species (e.g. *Anguis fragilis*) listed in category 10). In terms of the IUCN status categories (IUCN 1988), the SEH category 1 is equivalent to 'Endangered', while categories 2 and 3 include 'Vulnerable', 'Rare' and some 'Indeterminate' species.

Most subspecies were omitted from the assessment of conservation status, except for a few very distinct subspecies, or for noted island forms or evolving groups. It is encouraging to note that since the first assessment was produced, eight distinctive subspecies have been elevated to full species, while two more are expected to be confirmed as species and a further two are under consideration for species status. The current assessment now covers taxa found in Cyprus, Madeira and selected species occurring in Turkey. However, much more field assessment is needed in Turkey and further consideration needs to be given to some species found in that country whose range extends to the Middle East. European Soviet Union has not been adequately covered, although a handful of their Red Data List species are included.

Reference

IUCN (1988) *Red List of threatened animals*. IUCN, Cambridge.

Table 2: Threatened European reptiles and amphibians. According to IUCN definitions, category 1 is equivalent to 'Endangered'; categories 2 and 3 include 'Vulnerable', 'Rare' and 'Indeterminate'.

Category 1	Category 2	Category 3
Salamandra (atra) aurorae	*Chioglossa lusitanica*	*Mertensiella luschani*
Proteus anguinus	*Triturus helveticus puncillatus*	*Mertensiella caucasica*
Alytes muletensis	*Speleomantes ambrosii*	*Salamandrina terdigitata*
Pelobates fuscus insubricus	*Speleomantes flavus*	*Euproctus asper*
	Speleomantes imperialis	*Euproctus montanus*
	Speleomantes supramontis	*Euproctus platycephalus*
Rana latastei		*Triturus alpestris cyreni*
Rana holtzi		*Triturus vittatus*
	Bombina bombina	*Triturus boscai*
	Discoglossus jeanneae	*Speleomantes genei*
		Neurergus crocatus
Testudo hermanni hermanni	*Testudo marginata*	
Caretta caretta	*Trionyx triunguis*	*Discoglossus sardus*
Chelonia mydas		*Hyla sarda*
*Dermochelys coriacea**		
	Phyllodactylus europaeus	*Testudo hermanni boettgeri*
Gallotia simonyi	*Cyrtopodion koschyi baroni*	*Testudo graeca*
Podarcis muralis muellerlorenzi	*Chamaeleo chamaeleon*	*Emys orbicularis*
Podarcis hispanica atrata	*Algyroides moreoticus*	*Trionyx euphraticus*
Podarcis lilfordi group	*Algyroides marchi*	
Podarcis pityusensis group	*Lacerta monticola*	*Tarentola gomerensis*
Podarcis sicula coerulea	*Lacerta bedriagae*	*Algyroides nigropunctatus*
Podarcis sicula carbonensis	*Lacerta horvathi*	
	Lacerta uzzelli	
Vipera (ursinii) rakosiensis		

Vipera aspis montecristi
Vipera schweizeri
Vipera kaznakovi
Vipera bulgardaghica +
Vipera wagneri

Eremias suphani
Varanus griseus

Coluber cypriensis
Coluber rubriceps
Natrix natrix cetti
Natrix natrix corsa
Vipera raddei
Vipera ursinii
Vipera barani

Gallotia stehlini
Gallotia atlantica group
Lacerta graeca
Lacerta lepida
Lacerta princeps kurdistanica
Lacerta schreiberi
Podarcis bocagei
Podarcis wagleriana
Podarcis filfolensis
Podarcis melisellensis
Podarcis peloponnesiaca
Podarcis milensis
Chalcides viridanus
Ophiomorus punctatissimus

Eryx jaculus
Coluber caspius
Coluber hippocrepis
Coluber laurenti
Coluber najadum

Rhynchocalamus satunini
Vipera seoanei
Vipera latasti
Vipera xanthina

*D. coriacea may no longer breed in the Mediterranean;
+ V. bulgardaghica may be extinct.

Part Two

Review of Species and Habitat
Conservation Priorities

4

Key Species in the Council of Europe Area

FIRE-BELLIED TOAD
Bombina bombina

Biology

This is a small, warty, aquatic member of the Discoglossidae, with a round or triangular pupil, flat body, dark dorsal side and a bright red belly (Plate 1). Throughout its range, *B. bombina* is mainly a lowland species, occurring in marshy or wet grasslands, along river valleys, in pastures with small, shallow lakes or ponds, and in coastal wetlands. It prefers shallow, often temporary ponds without inlets or outlets, and with extensive flooded shores during the spring. Short grassland surrounding the ponds is essential as a feeding area at night. Terrestrial hibernation places, such as stone walls, logs, or forest, within a few hundred metres from the pond, are important.

The behavioural and ecological demands of the species vary considerably over its geographical range. Adults are physiologically more tolerant of variations in habitat than the more sensitive juveniles. All age groups normally hibernate on land. After emerging in late March to early May, the animals move to the nearest body of water, which may not necessarily be the spawning pond. The distance between the place of hibernation and the spawning pond is normally a few hundred metres, rarely up to 800m. The mating period, which lasts a few weeks, varies over different parts of the range between mid April and early June. Clean and shallow water with dense vegetation is normally chosen.

Spawning places are often temporarily flooded areas, and the flooding itself may be an important factor in inducing reproductive behaviour. Males from a large area normally aggregate in one spawning place, calling males having circular territories with a radius of 1-1.5m. Each female deposits between 80 and 300 eggs in clumps of 15-40 attached to submerged vegetation 15 to 40cm under the water surface. The development from egg to metamorphosis is temperature-dependent, varying between 60 and 90 days. The time and temperature required for tadpole development is believed to be a critical factor in the survival of the north-western populations in Scandinavia. Adults mainly feed at night on invertebrates in the inner littoral zone, or in the immediate vicinity of the pond. Sometimes adults leave the pond in late summer and move to swampy meadows, where they live until early autumn and hibernation.

Past and Present Distribution

B. bombina has a wide distribution (Figure 5) ranging from southern Sweden and south-eastern Denmark, eastwards through the Soviet Union to about 65° E in the Ural Mountains and north to about 57.2° N; south-east to just north of the Caspian Sea, and south to about 43° N in the Caucasian Mountains; its southern limits follow the Black Sea through Romania, Bulgaria, eastern Yugoslavia, western Greece, Hungary, Austria, Czechoslovakia, the German Democratic Republic and to about 10°E in the north-east of the Federal Republic of Germany. The CoE range states are considered below.

Sweden

In the middle of the last century the species was widespread in southern and western parts of Scania, but during the last 100 years it has continuously declined. For 50 years it was restricted to only one locality, a coastal area in the north-west of Scania, where it eventually became extinct in 1960. In 1983 an official project was commenced to reintroduce the species into four selected areas in Scania.

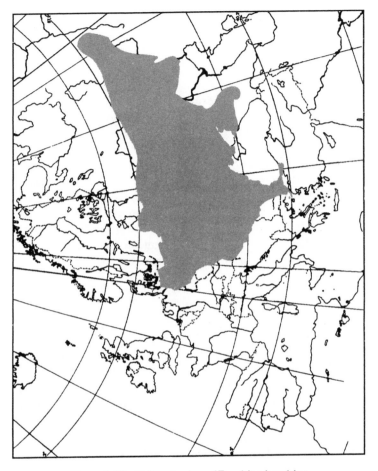

Figure 5: World Distribution of Bombina bombina

Denmark

During the last few hundred years *B. bombina* has been introduced to many localities in Denmark, and so its natural range cannot be accurately defined. It is likely, however, to have included the islands of Fyen, Sjaelland, Lolland, Falster and Moen, as well as many smaller islands in the southern and eastern Danish archipelago. The present distribution of 11 or 12 isolated populations extends over the exposed and dry lowland areas along Storebaelt, on southern Sjaelland, and in the archipelago south of Fyen.

Federal Republic of Germany

In the Federal Republic of Germany the range of *B. bombina* once included most wetland areas in Schleswig-Holstein, south to the River Elbe in the eastern part of Lower Saxony (Wendland). The range also included the lowlands along the River Aller, central-eastern parts of Lower Saxony, and possibly Weser. The present population in Schleswig-Holstein is concentrated in the coastal, central and eastern parts of the 'Ostlichen Hugelland', including the island of Fehmarn, the 'Ostholsteinische Seengebiet', and the 'Ratzeburger Seenplatte'. The range south of the River Elbe is largely unchanged, but is now more fragmented in the valley of the Aller. In the central-eastern part of Lower Saxony the species has died out.

Austria

The past distribution of *B. bombina* in Austria is not known in detail, but available evidence suggests that no major changes have taken place during the past few hundred years. Nevertheless, the present distribution is more fragmented due to habitat destruction in many areas. The range includes the northern lowlands, mainly along the River Donau from Krems to Hainburg, in the Weinviertel to Horner Becken, Marchfeld and Steinfeld. The area east of Lake Neusiedl is probably the most important part of the Austrian range. The species also occurs in other lowland areas of Burgenland and in a small part of eastern Steiermark.

Turkey and Greece

Information from these two countries is rather limited, the species having only recently come to light in some cases, so its status and range in the region is not fully known. *B. bombina* is reported from at least four localities in Thrace and the species seems to be fairly widespread in the Lake Sapanca region of north-west Anatolia. There are four reported localities in the north-east of Greece, to the east of Alexandoupolis.

Reasons for Decline and Current Threats

The species formerly occurred in uncultivated and unditched swampy areas and pastures, habitats which have now been greatly reduced with the advent of modern, more intensive farming methods.

Only one of the known Swedish localities has remained more or less untouched, while all the others have been damaged or destroyed by road construction, forestry, cultivation and drainage. In Denmark the species used to be more common and widespread, but similar factors are responsible for the serious decrease in population numbers during the last 100 years. In the middle of the last century more than 50 different populations were known, but by the 1940's only about 20 of these remained. Today, there are just four stable populations, each with several ponds and supporting more than 100 adult toads, in addition to a few populations with one or two ponds and 10 to 50 adults.

Several of the present Danish populations are now isolated in small patches of suitable habitat in large cultivated fields, with a severe scarcity of hibernation places, very restricted feeding areas, and with continually deteriorating water quality as a result of eutrophication and pollution. Some breeding ponds in uncultivated pastures are no longer suitable because of shading by trees and floating vegetation, which reduces the heating of the surface water. The species appears to be most sensitive to these environmental changes in the northern part of its range.

Its distribution in most parts of the Federal Republic of Germany and Austria seems to be largely the same as that known in the beginning of this century, but the total number of populations and their actual density has decreased seriously, particularly in Germany. The causes for this decline are the same as in the Nordic countries, namely the habitat deterioration and the fragmentation and isolation of populations, owing to more intensive cultivation.

The regulation of water levels in many rivers has reduced natural spring flooding, and this may be the principal cause for the loss of the species in the Aller River valley and some other localities. In most areas, drainage, filling in of ponds, construction of levées near to rivers, cultivation of pasture land, pollution of water by fertilisers and pesticides, and the construction of roads and houses are the obvious causes for the decrease. Even though a few areas in Germany still have stable populations, the recent loss of populations is very pronounced (in Lower Saxony about 60 per cent since 1915), and the remaining animals live in progressively diminishing patches of suitable habitat.

Conservation Measures Achieved

In Sweden, Denmark, the Federal Republic of Germany and Austria the species is given nominal protection under national statutes. In Sweden the locality in north-western Scania is a nature reserve. In Denmark several breeding ponds are protected in important areas, and it is illegal to destroy its habitat, though several localities have been lost in spite of this. In the Federal Republic of Germany some breeding areas receive incidental protection, and several of those in Lower Saxony are given some degree of protection. In Austria some populations are within nature reserves, but no areas or ponds are protected mainly or exclusively for *B. bombina*. Neither the species or its sites receive protection in Turkey, nor are its habitats protected in Greece, although some sites may occasionally coincide with otherwise designated areas. This is a somewhat anomalous situation, as both countries have long ratified the Berne Convention and Appendix II status under the Convention requires strict protection for *B. bombina* and its habitat.

Conservation Measures Proposed

The conservation of this species is important if only for its value as an ecological indicator of a particularly rich type of lowland habitat, valuable for many plants and invertebrates. The protection of *B. bombina* habitat should include its breeding (and feeding) ponds, terrestrial feeding zones surrounding the waterbodies, and hibernation places. The exact area needed depends on the landscape, topography, number and quality of ponds and distance to hibernation places. Natural spring flooding of the pond system must be guaranteed and any possible outlets from the ponds blocked. Vegetation surrounding the ponds must be kept low, to ensure maximum insolation. This can be achieved through a balanced grazing regime, or by regular mowing. Bushes on the northern side of the ponds may serve as wind breaks without shading the sun.

The pond water must be clean and clear with much submerged vegetation. Scattered floating vegetation may have a positive effect by reducing wind movements in the water, but when the surface is completely covered it delays the heating up of the water. Fertilisers or pesticides should not be used in the vicinity of the ponds. The renovation of old, or the construction of new breeding sites can sometimes be useful. For conservation programmes to be effective in the longer term, they should not only preserve and safeguard the remaining populations, but should also ensure genetic exchange between populations, which are becoming increasingly isolated. In some regions, new habitat with suitable breeding ponds should be created between existing isolated populations, in order to open up potential migration corridors.

Recently, a Scandinavian *Bombina* research group was set up with the aim of identifying the habitat requirements for the species on the north-western edge of its range.

The Standing Committee of the Berne Convention has recommended (Appendix I) that the most important sites at Storebaelt, southern Sjaelland and the archipelago south of Fyon in Denmark, and the Pevestorfer Elvwiesen in West Germany should be protected.

Biogenetic Reserves are not being proposed for Sweden until the recent reintroduction attempts have been shown to be successful. Five different reserves have been proposed for Denmark where the remaining populations are living in somewhat diverse habitats. This will ensure that all the important populations and their habitat types will be given the best possible protection. The Danish nature conservation authorities have reacted positively to this recommendation. In the Federal Republic of Germany one large Biogenetic Reserve has been selected, which at present is only partly protected as a landscape reserve although also directly adjacent to a Ramsar Site. Finally, a survey for this species should be carried out in the East European countries which form the core of *Bombina*'s range with a view to identifying important sites and conservation needs.

MALLORCAN MIDWIFE TOAD
Alytes muletensis

Biology

This is a small discoglossid toad, creamy white with olivaceous blotches, of comparatively slender build and with strikingly large and prominent eyes (Plate 2). Like other midwife toads, the males have a musical single-noted mating call, they mate on land, and the males transport and 'care for' the resultant string of eggs which are wrapped around the hind limbs. The eggs, however, are far fewer and much larger than those produced by the other two *Alytes* species, with a maximum of twenty so far recorded.

These toads live in steep-sided limestone gorges (Figure 6), eroded by mountain torrents of only 50-300m in length, but falling precipitously. Glassy chutes separate water-scoured and sculptured basins, and the toads use the more permanent of the pools to support their tadpoles through to metamorphosis (Plate 3). The tadpoles are efficient filter feeders in these oligotrophic waters and they are also able to withstand the rapid flows and turbulence occurring in the pools in between the periods of stagnation during the summer. The adult toads are adept climbers and spend much of the day wedged away, often communally, in narrow clefts and crevices in the limestone rocks and gorge walls, as well as under boulders in the drier parts of the torrent bed.

Since sunlight hardly penetrates the deep gorges and owing to the extremes of flow, the vegetation cover is sparse. A predominantly moss and fern community occupies the waterfall spray zone, with an *Eucladio-Adiantetum* complex and the endemic *Hypocrepidetum balearici* being confined to the more hospitable parts of the gorge wall together with scattered trees. The sparse vegetation nevertheless supports a good supply of invertebrate food for the toads.

The inaccessibility of the gorges provides security from predation by various mammal species (whose corpses are sometimes found at the foot of the gorges) as well as from the specialist amphibian-eating snake *Natrix maura*. Competition from *Rana perezi* is ruled out by the adverse habitat conditions.

Figure 6: Rock fissures with torrents provide a last refuge for
A. muletensis; *safe from predators but hard work to survey!*
(Photo: J. Mayol)

Past and Present Distribution

A. muletensis was only discovered to be extant in 1980: before then it was known only from sub-fossil remains which showed that it had occurred in various parts of the Gimnesias Islands of the Balearics (i.e. Mallorca and Menorca). Although these findings represent the incidental discoveries of investigations into selected archaeological sites and caves, they nevertheless reveal a much more widespread distribution within these islands (including lowland habitats), as recently as 1,800 years ago. Today, however, these toads are confined to seven mountain torrents in the limestone mountains of the Serra de Tramuntana in northern Mallorca. Two other torrents have had recent, but no longer confirmed, records. The population numbers between 300 and 700 adult pairs.

Reasons for Decline and Current Threats

The most popular explanation for the range contraction of *A. muletensis* is man's introduction of the predatory *Natrix maura*, whether intentionally (for Roman religious purposes), or more likely accidentally. Certainly it is noticeable from the sub-fossil record that as the snakes appeared, the toads soon disappeared. It is clear that the limestone gorges are the only freshwater habitat free of these snakes. Potential competition from *Rana perezei* is ruled out by the adverse habitat conditions.

To account for the decline and apparent loss of two of the nine recent *A. muletensis* populations and perhaps the low populations of another three, one cannot help but point the finger of suspicion at water barrage operations, whether for large reservoirs for the city of Palma, or for the many smaller agricultural impoundments. The connections within limestone catchment areas, above and below ground, are highly complex and difficult to predict, and do not appear to have been studied in Serra de Tramuntana. Any such impoundment could impede the flow to the gorge pools, especially in a drought period, and subsequent abstraction would change the natural water regime on which this rare toad depends.

Moreover, a large fruit farm is situated on a plateau within the toad's range, directly above one torrent and perhaps indirectly above others. The risks from accidental contamination of the water courses by pesticides and/or fertilisers must be recognised, even though there is a local voluntary agreement on their use. Other potential problems could arise from:

- the stocking of predatory fish, such as trout, in the reservoirs above the toad's breeding gorges;
- the increasing use of the gorges for rock climbing, with its associated disturbance and pollution which is already evident;
- vegetation changes and erosion resulting from local burning and over-grazing of the hillsides above the gorges.

From experience with other rare amphibians, collection for either museum or vivarium purposes, could become a real threat to the *A. muletensis* populations if or when the value of specimens offsets the difficulties of access.

Conservation Measures Achieved

In partial response to the provisions of the Berne Convention *A. muletensis* itself is strictly protected under Spanish national law. However, there are as yet no habitat provisions, and a long-standing proposal for a national 'Natural Park' has recently been abandoned in the face of local opposition.

The first releases of captive stock reared at Jersey and Frankfurt Zoos have recently taken place with the aim of re-establishing populations of *A. muletensis* in torrents within their former range.

Conservation Measures Proposed

An international 'Biogenetic Reserve' of 26,200 ha should be established for *A. muletensis*, encompassing eight of the nine torrents and their water catchment. By its modest extension north-westwards, such a reserve would also include the endemic plants of the Formantor peninsula, the islet of Colomer where *Podarcis lilfordi* occurs (see below), and the feeding and breeding habitat of osprey (*Pandion haliaetus*), peregrine (*Falco peregrinus*) and Eleonora's falcon (*Falco eleonorae*) as well as the rare and endangered black vulture (*Aegypius monachus*). The proposed reserve (Figure 7) is a karst landscape of limestone mountain and sea cliffs, with rocky areas, torrents, woods of low evergreen oaks and settlement areas typically with olive groves. The main plant associations are oak (*Quercetum illicis galloprovinciale*), maquis (*Oleo ceratonion*), on the cliffs and gorge walls *Hypocrepidetum balearici*, and in exposed locations, *Teucrietum subspinosi*. Within this area there would be a need to counter the threats listed above, especially fruit farming; to prevent any further water impoundment and abstraction (with a long-term plan to redress some of the existing installations); and to draw up contingency plans to resist collection of *A. muletensis*, or encroachment by *Natrix maura*. So far, a core area of 8,000ha has been provisionally agreed by delegates to the CoE Environment Committee in 1988 but this has not yet been implemented.

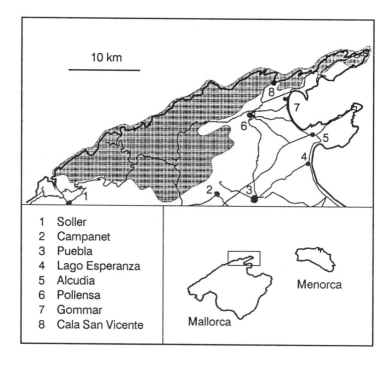

1 Soller
2 Campanet
3 Puebla
4 Lago Esperanza
5 Alcudia
6 Pollensa
7 Gommar
8 Cala San Vicente

Figure 7: Proposed Biogenetic Reserve for Alytes muletensis *in the Serra de Tramuntana, Northern Mallorca.*

ITALIAN SPADEFOOT
Pelobates fuscus insubricus

Biology

This is a small amphibian with characters between a frog and a toad. Normally the animals are strongly coloured with a lot of fine red dots, and are characterised by a vertical pupil and the strikingly large tubercle at the base of the hind foot (the 'spade foot'). Discovered in 1873 by E. Cornalia at Noverasco and Mirasole, near Milano, the animal was described as a new species. However, the classification of this form was a long-debated issue until, at the end of the last century, it was acknowledged to be a new subspecies *'insubricus'* of *Pelobates fuscus*, zoogeographically separated from other populations by the Alps. In the early years of this century, a whole series of localities were discovered and many animals placed in museum collections. After 1920, however, only a few further localities were found, and publications about the animal practically ceased.

Even now, the taxonomic status of this form is not absolutely clear. Its distribution is totally isolated from the area of the nominate form *P. f. fuscus*, and it lives under different conditions. This suggests that it could well be a separate species. Detailed genetic investigations are planned, and would greatly help to assess this animal's international conservation status. While there is no more precise information, this animal should be treated as a special form, for which protection is absolutely necessary.

Past and Present Distribution

S. Bruno, E. Burattini and A. Casale reviewed all the information on *P. f. insubricus*, and carried out a survey in the early 1970s. Their report contains a distribution map (Figure 8), though without a list of exact localities and without reference to the data collected. The authors mention 50 older localities, of which only three were still extant in 1974. They also succeeded in finding 12 hitherto unknown localities. Hence, the known sites in 1974 amounted to 15, but the information on the precise location of these is not available. The second part of the survey contained detailed data on its habitat, ecology and life-history in the Po floodplain.

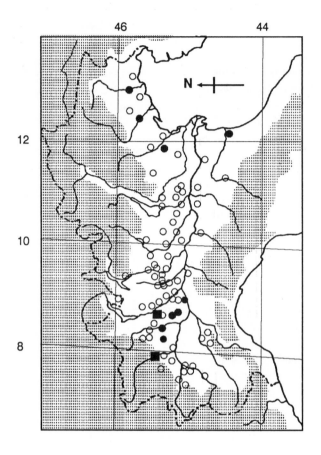

Figure 8: Occurrence of Pelobates fuscus insubricus *in the Po floodplain. Shaded area is over 700m altitude.*

○ *records prior to 1974*

● *single records after 1974*

■ *confirmed stable populations*

Originally, *P. f. insubricus* was distributed over the whole Padano-Venetian plain, with outlying localities in Monfalcone (east), Ravenna (south), Valle di Susa (west) and Lugano in Switzerland (north). The range was very similar to that of *Rana latastei*, with the exception of Istria (Yugoslavia) where that species also occurs. Typical habitats include sandy areas, heathlands and deciduous woodland on light soils.

Since the survey mentioned above, nine other sites have come to light, widely distributed over the whole area, some of them published, others not. In four cases, especially the two easternmost sites, only tadpoles were found, and there must be some doubt over the correct identification, since the tadpoles of *Rana esculenta* and *R. catesbiana* can also be very large (8-10cm) and display striking similarities with those of *P. f. insubricus*.

Only two localities are situated in the eastern part of the Po floodplain, others are found in a relatively narrow area north of the Po between Milano and Torino, mostly in the large sandy stretches between the rivers Sesia, Ticino and Po, where the prevailing habitats are certainly better than elsewhere. However, it is possible that the concentration of sites in this area results from the fact that the eminent herpetologists who have worked here have looked specifically for this form; this has not been the case in most of the other Po regions.

Between 1981 and 1984, V. Ferri discovered tadpoles of *P. f. insubricus* in a rice paddy several kilometres east of Novara, not far from the river Ticino. In 1984 and 1985, K. Grossenbacher and others found tadpoles in several different rice paddies in the same region, as well as a few adults. This is almost certainly an area where *P. f. insubricus* occurs in good numbers, and there is no other known region where it can otherwise be found with certainty. The rice paddies supporting *P. f. insubricus* are distributed over a 4.5 kilometre stretch of the valley. Other paddies in the same area were surveyed, without result. It is not yet known where the adults go during the non-breeding season.

The rice paddies are located in an agricultural area which is not very intensively farmed. Several of them border woodland which extends to the Ticino river, about 500m away. The river itself flows in a valley with steep, wooded slopes, and moist deciduous woodland grows alongside the river. On the steep slopes and near the rice paddy fields, there are dry woody stretches, patches of heathland with birches (*Betula* spp.) and heather (*Calluna vulgaris*) and some rough pastures. The rice paddies supporting the tadpoles are recent and since there will be further new rice paddies, it will be interesting to observe whether these are more favoured by *P. f. insubricus* than the older ones. Indeed, tadpoles were often found at places where the rice had not germinated and where marsh plants grew instead (including *Typha latifolia*, *Sparganium ramosum*, *Alisma plantago-aquatica*, *Schoenoplectus mucronatus*, and *Eleocharis obtusa*). In such places, water apparently stays longer than in the other parts of the rice paddies. It is also likely that they are less intensively treated with fertilisers and pesticides, so that the marsh plants and amphibian tadpoles are able to thrive.

Reproduction is obviously limited with respect to time, because of the cultivation of the rice; the rice paddies are empty in winter and filled with water only in mid April. During July, they mostly dry up again. Thus, tadpoles have no more than three months to develop. Belated spawning or hibernation of tadpoles, which is not infrequent in *Pelobates fuscus fuscus* (the common spadefoot), are not possible under these conditions. Tadpoles can usually develop, however, because the temperature of the water in June/July rises very high (e.g. 33°C at the beginning of June) in the shallow fields (average of 10-30cm deep).

Reasons for Decline

We have so little information about this subspecies that even the reasons for its decline are not clear. Certainly many of its original habitats (heathlands, river banks, deciduous woodlands) have been destroyed, but as the currently known breeding places are rice paddies, of which several thousand exist in the Po floodplain, other factors such as water pollution and pesticides must be responsible for the comparatively recent and severe loss of numbers.

Conservation Measures Achieved

None of the known breeding sites lies within nature reserves. It is possible that some populations may occur along the river Ticino, which includes a natural park (Parco naturale della Valle Ticino), but there is no confirmation of this.

Conservation Measures Proposed

It is at present impossible, for various reasons, to create a Biogenetic Reserve for *P. f. insubricus*, even though the species occurs close to the border of the natural park of Ticino, which is a protected area. Up to now, no spadefoots have been found in the park itself. The rice paddies are created artificially and intensively cultivated. It is remarkable that tadpoles have been found only in this man-made habitat, and several questions about the biology of the animal still require answers, for example:

- where do the adults live?
- are newly prepared rice paddies more likely than others to support spadefoots?
- are the colonised rice paddies less intensively treated with fertilisers and pesticides?
- do spadefoots also occur in the surrounding area such as on the larger sandbanks of the River Ticino, or in neighbouring gravel-pits, or in other rice paddies?

It would be highly desirable to create a new pond in the area, which would fill the following conditions: no rice culture; no fish; no *Rana catesbiana* (a species which has already been naturalised in this region), and if possible, water all year round. It should measure 20m by 10m and have a maximum depth of 1m. This pond would serve the purpose of investigating the reproduction of *P. f. fuscus*.

Of course, *P. f. insubricus* might occur elsewhere in the Po floodplain. No other amphibian species in Europe leads such a secretive life, so it is particularly difficult to find reliable clues as to its presence. As long as there is no other information, it is essential that this region be thoroughly surveyed, and that parts of it are protected in due course. The Standing Committee of the Berne Convention has accepted (Appendix I) that the Parco del Ticino in Italy should be extended to cover adjacent *P. f. insubricus* breeding sites.

ITALIAN AGILE FROG
Rana latastei

Biology

This is a rather small, brown frog. Typical characters are a uniform red-brown colour on the upper side, a dark brown throat with a fine clear line in the centre, a clear band in the upper jaw between the corner of the mouth and the eye, a small tympanum and long hindlegs (Plate 4).

The original habitat of *R. latastei* was semi-moist deciduous forests currently classified as the *Querco-Carpinetum boreoitalicum* association. Elsewhere, it is always found in floodplains with high water tables, typically by a small stream, river or lake with moist deciduous forest, some swampy ground and a lush herbaceous ground flora. The highest site presently known is Levic (Trento) at 440m above sea level.

Individuals show no tendency to migrate, always living close to their spawning sites. The breeding season reaches peak activity in March, when small clumps of eggs are deposited in the backwaters of streams, in ditches, or in small ponds. The favoured situation would appear to be shallow, slowly flowing water, although egg clumps can sometimes be deposited in still water. The probable normal mating pattern was recorded along the rivers Lambro (Brianza, north of Milano) and Begotta (Bosco della Fontana, near Mantova). Males distribute themselves several metres from each other and produce their weak mating call. The mating calls are normally emitted underwater, or with the head above water.

The typical population structure of *R. latastei* is as follows: in the spring a great part of the breeding population consists of small, one-year old animals with a body length of 37-42mm. Most of the newly metamorphosed individuals reach sexual maturity in the following spring. By their first autumn these animals attain a body length of 28-42mm (average 35mm) and in the best sites they can be found in numbers of several hundreds. On the other hand, in autumn, adults larger than 45mm (up to 62mm) are rare. As many fewer frogs are found in the following spring, it is very likely that they are subject to high mortality during winter hibernation. The mortality of adults at the breeding place may also be high. In fact, observations of adults after breeding time and through the whole summer are rare, and the proportion of adults in the autumn population is low. It follows that *R. latastei* is characterized by a rapid population turnover and a highly fluctuating population size. The occurrence of a particularly successful reproductive season can therefore produce a large, though usually temporary, increase in the size of the autumn population.

The spatial distribution of the adults also varies with the season. In the spring, the forest floor is relatively bare, humidity is often at its lowest and only a few animals are normally encountered away from the breeding sites. During the late spring, summer and early autumn, a rich vegetation is produced on the forest floor and the frogs' activity increases greatly. After the end of spawning, however, adult behaviour and distribution are highly influenced by ground water availability and prevailing weather conditions, particularly as determined by the onset of autumn rainfall. In the years when the latter were particularly scarce or delayed (as in September 1985), the young adults are mainly concentrated in the lush vegetation growing along ditches and on the river banks, emerging at night to sit on the dewy, broad leaves of *Plantago major*.

Past and Present Distribution

R. latastei is virtually confined to the CoE area, primarily to the lowlands of the Padano-Venetian plains of Italy, Switzerland and into northern Yugoslavia (Figure 9). However, various types of human impacts have combined to restrict it to about 35 relict populations. These are scattered over an area comprising North Istria, Ravenna, Vercelli and Chiasso. It is extinct at Redecessio (Milano), the site where it was first collected and described by Boulenger.

Reasons for Decline and Current Threats

Several populations live within existing reserves, for example: Parco naturale della Valle del Ticino, Torbiere del Bassone di Albate and Lago Alserio, and Seseslio in Switzerland. But the reason for creating these reserves was never the existence of *R. latastei* and they are not managed with this species in mind. The size and status of the populations in these localities are low. The three surviving populations in Switzerland are rather small, the habitat far from optimal

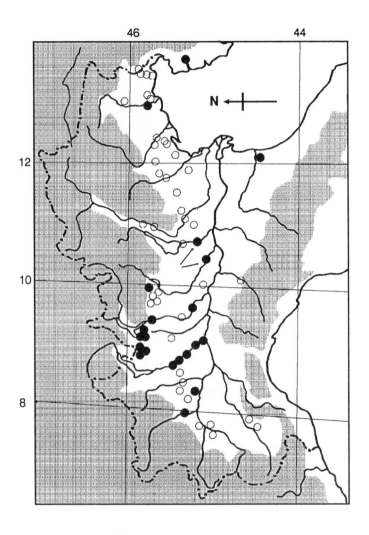

Figure 9: Occurrence of Rana latastei *in the Po floodplain.*
Shaded area is over 700m altitude.

○   *records prior to 1977*
●   *confirmed localities*
⟶   *proposed Biogenetic Reserves*

and threatened for several reasons: two of the 'reserves' are not adequately protected or managed and the third was badly damaged.

Conservation Measures Achieved

The damaged Swiss site mentioned above has now been restored, enhanced and properly protected.

Conservation Measures Proposed

Any long term conservation policy for *R. latastei* should aim for the establishment of at least two reserves, namely Bosco della Fontana and Le Bine. These sites are described below.

Bosco della Fontana

This is a wooded area of 232ha situated near the town of Mantova, in Lombardy which has been managed as a protected area since the times of the Dukes of Mantova. Its present status dates back to 1910 when it was declared a Natural Forest Reserve of the Forestry Department (Demanio Forestale dello Stato). In 1976 it became an IUCN 'Natural Oriented Reserve', and the capture of frogs is officially forbidden. The western third of the forest is closed to the public, while the eastern two-thirds are open to the public during the day and run as a 'woodland park'.

Bosco della Fontana represents one of the last remnants of the primeval riverine forests that once covered most of the Padano-Venetian plains. Its vegetation is still very close to the original (Tomaselli 1970), and includes trees such as *Quercus robur, Q.cerris, Fraxinus ornus* and *Carpinus betulus,* with *Lonicera xylosteum, Cornus mas* and *Prunus avium* among the shrubs. The herbaceous layer consists of *Ruscus aculeatus, Vinca major, Mercurialis perennis, Hedera helix* and *Ajuga reptans.* Active efforts are presently being made by the Forestry Department (Corpo Forestale dello Stato) to remove exotic ornamental trees from the forest.

A small river (la Begotta) crosses the forest. Its usually clean and clear calcareous waters serve as the main spawning site, together with some spring-fed canals and ditches. The usually high water-table and the lush herbaceous vegetation produce a very high humidity, which is the other main reason for the relative abundance of *R. latastei* here (Plate 5). Pozzi (1980) estimated an autumn density of 57-73 frogs per hectare, but subsequent SEH visits have found much lower densities and far less spawn clumps than would otherwise be expected. It should be remembered, however, that the number of subadult individuals observed in autumn may not be strictly related to the population size in the following spring, as a consequence of potentially fluctuating winter mortality rates. Moreover, it seems likely that the whole forest may not now be humid enough for uniform distribution of the species. This is suggested by the fact that SEH records come mainly from along the stream and in the south-eastern area. Nevertheless, the SEH estimate of some 5,000 adult frogs (spring population) is an order of magnitude greater than any other surviving Swiss or Italian population (apart from Le Bine), and indeed is probably more than the combined total of all other sites (again, excluding Le Bine).

Although the present situation for *R. latastei* at Bosco della Fontana appears to be good, with a population certainly large enough to be viable in the long-term, recent surveys indicate that the ecological status of the reserve is deteriorating. The greatest problem is that the water-table inside the forest is steadily falling, even after making appropriate allowances for the low winter and spring rainfalls of the past three years. For example, in May the water-table in a large pit in the north of the forest was 1.55m below the surface, whereas the Forestry Department reported a level of not less than 80cm below ground some 20 years earlier. As a consequence, the size and number of suitable frog breeding sites are declining, and this probably accounts for the observed recent decrease in the population. During the last two years, the Forestry Department has tried to reverse the drying trend by pumping water into the ditches which cross the forest, mainly from canals on the south-west border. However, the pumping had to be suspended following protests from various sources and because of water shortages in the nearby town of Mantova. While the lowering of the water-table in summer is due mainly to the excessive and scarcely controlled pumping from the canal system from the River Mincio for agricultural use, this does not entirely account for the relatively low water during early spring which may be a reflection of the generally lowered water table throughout the Po Valley. This is probably the result of abstraction for large towns like Milano and even Mantova itself. The principal conservation measures required in Bosco della Fontana may be summarised as follows:

-   Action to reverse the drying out trend, which addresses the practical difficulties arising from the location of this surviving riverine forest in the middle of the intensive agriculture of the Po floodplain, and close to the town of Mantova.
-   Controlling, and to any possible extent preventing, pumping of ground water from the catchment area serving the forest.
-   Re-pumping water from the canals into the forest ditches which were apparently created for this purpose.
-   Creation of new ponds in the most secluded parts of the forest, ideally the part now closed to normal public access.
-   All ponds and ditches should be replenished with water by mid-February to ensure that they are in good condition for the onset of *R. latastei* breeding (late February to early March, in early seasons).
-   In general, the water levels of of the ditches and ponds should be kept as high as possible.

Le Bine

This site is an old river branch along the river Olio between Cremona and Mantova. Parts of the site are presently a WWF reserve, established to protect an important nesting colony of several species of waterbirds. The ecological integrity of this wood-land is far less satisfactory than that of Bosco della Fontana, because the inner part consists of a poplar plantation. Along the old branch and the dikes (a system of canal and ditches that was dug in the past to control the ground-water level), the soil is covered by a rich herbaceous vegetation. Under the poplar plantation the vegetation is sparse or totally absent, but even so, *R. latastei* occurs here if the ground is moist. The main reason for proposing the whole of this site as a Biogenetic Reserve is the extremely high population of *R. latastei*, apparently because of optimal breeding conditions. It is certainly the largest surviving population presently known. Should the Bosco della Fontana reserve further deteriorate, this site could conceivably conserve the species in the long-term. The possibility that a more natural vegetation cover can be encouraged is certainly not to be ruled out.

THE MARINE TURTLES

Four of the five circumglobal sea turtle species have been recorded in European waters, and of these the green turtle *Chelonia mydas* and loggerhead *Caretta caretta* continue to breed in the Mediterranean but their situation there, as elsewhere in their range, is very grave. Because of the great similarity between these two turtles in terms of biology, nesting distribution and status, they are considered together in the following account.

Biology

For those hatchlings which successfully reach the comparative safety of the open sea there follows a very long period of feeding and growth to maturity, thought to be up to 25 years for *Caretta* and some 50 years for *Chelonia*. During their pelagic existence, the young feed on plankton and young fish. As they approach maturity and adopt adult feeding habits, *Chelonia* becomes more or less entirely herbivorous and feeds on sea-grasses, while *Caretta* feeds on jelly-fish, benthic shellfish and crustaceans which are crushed by its large powerful jaws.

Figure 10: Female Caretta caretta *nesting at night, watched quietly by carefully controlled 'eco-tourists' (photo: K. Corbett).*

58

Adult turtles undertake lengthy migrations probably to the general coastal area, if not the exact beach, where they hatched. Males may assemble each spring, but the females return only every two to three years to breed, using the interim years to renew their fat reserves for the next season's egg-laying.

In the Mediterranean, female turtles may lay two to three clutches during the summer (Figure 10), each of around 110 eggs (generally a little less for *Caretta* and rather more for *Chelonia*). Nest sites are inspected and selected by an alert and cautious female. 'False crawls' tend to increase in frequency when there is human disturbance. Soft sands are preferred and the favoured location is deeper, slumped sand located at the foot of a dune ridge or cliff. The average distance from the shore for nesting may be 15-20 metres, but the overall range may be 5-70 metres or more depending on the type of beach and its slope characteristics. Steep beaches with nests nearer but well above the sea may mean there is less hatchling predation and these beaches are therefore of a high conservation priority.

The hole for egg-laying is dug with a deep, cylindrical egg chamber usually situated at the end of the nest facing the sea. On completion of egg-laying, the nest is covered up and attempts made to flatten and conceal it. Predators such as fox, dog, jackal and wild boar appear to be able to locate fresh nests, sometimes within minutes of completion (Figure 11).

After many weeks of incubation in the warm sand, at a depth of sufficient humidity (30cm for *Caretta*, 45cm for *Chelonia*), the first eggs hatch. These early hatchlings begin to climb up and so loosen the sand while the rest of the clutch continues to hatch over several days. At this stage, the nest is said to be 'activated'. Emergence occurs synchronously at night with the hatchlings struggling to crawl to the sea, attracted by the luminosity of the sea/sky interface. Predators such as the crab *Ocypode cursor* can take a heavy toll of the hatchlings during their passage across the beach.

Past and Present Distribution

The last confirmed nesting of leatherback turtles *Dermochelys coriacia* in the Mediterranean occurred in Sicily during the 1930s, although it is regularly seen or caught in Greek and Italian waters.

Figure 11: Turtle nest destroyed by a wild boar soon after laying. As the number of turtles declines, natural predation becomes ever more serious (photo: K. Corbett).

Kemps Ridley *Eretmochelys imbricata* has been sighted occasionally off the Atlantic coast, but there are no breeding records.

Breeding Distribution

The overall population of *Caretta* in the Mediterranean is probably around 3,000 nesting females per year, with perhaps 15,000 adults in all. Although some recruitment from Atlantic stocks might occur via the Straits of Gibraltar, numbers are generally declining. The most important nesting sites are at Zakynthos (Europe's largest with about 600 nesting females per year), the western Peloponnese and Rhodes in Greece and at a number of localities along the south Turkish coast. In addition, about 400 nests per year are distributed between east and west Cyprus, mainly at Karpas and around Akamas.

Caretta is now very rare or has even ceased to breed in Corsica, Sardinia, mainland Italy, Sicily, Lampedusa, Gozo, Crete, western Turkey, Lebanon, Israel, and Egypt. Its status in Syria is uncertain and it is doubtful whether there has ever been breeding in Algeria. Libya probably still has a modest number of breeding turtles (about 60 nests) within Kouf National Park. Tunisia has a similar number although more widely scattered along the eastern coast. Morocco may support nesting *Caretta* but no data are available.

Chelonia requires warmer water than *Caretta* and so in Europe it is confined to the eastern Mediterranean. It occurs mainly along the south-east coast of Turkey, around Cyprus and in Israel. Nesting is also reported (but unconfirmed) from Morocco. In the Mediterranean as a whole, the total number of nesting females could now be as low as 300 per year.

Enormous numbers of *Chelonia* were once found in Turkey, but today they are mainly confined to between Mersin and Samandag where there is an estimated maximum of 700 nests each year. In the 1940s, large herds were reported from this stretch of coast but unrestricted exploitation brought about the collapse of the turtle fishery by 1960. The Cyprus stronghold is now down to an estimated 200 nests each year with 75 mainly at Toxeftra in the west, and 125 in the east, mainly at Karpas. Fisheries off Palestine in the 1920s and 1930s also took a heavy toll of the same large stocks, with a two-man crew alone harvesting as many as 550 *Chelonia* per day. Between 1979 and 1982, there were still an estimated 3,000 nests in the area, but less than half this level appears to remain. There is no doubt that this species is gravely endangered in the Mediterranean and that its extinction is now a real possibility without prompt conservation intervention (Figure 12).

Figure 12: The last Chelonia mydas *leaving its nesting beach? Without prompt conservation action, this scene could soon become a reality (photo: C. Andren).*

Non-breeding Distribution

Caretta caretta over-winters in some numbers in the Adriatic, off Yumurtalik and Mersin in Turkey, and in the Gulf of Gabès in Tunisia. Movements around the rest of the Mediterranean are poorly known but some interesting evidence is now emerging as a result of accidental catches and from the recapture of tagged animals (mainly sub-adults) marked on beaches in Greece and Turkey. The Balearics are now known to be a feeding area for sub-adults, but it is not known whether these animals breed in the Mediterranean or whether they are from the Atlantic. Turtles tagged in Greece have been recovered not only from the Aegean and Adriatic, but also from Malta, Libya, Corsica, Sardinia and the Gulf of Gabès. A few turtles tagged in Italy and Turkey have also been recaptured in the Gulf of Gabès, but other evidence suggests that some of the Turkish *Caretta* population may be confined to local waters. The overall picture for *Caretta* is therefore of a population which uses a large area of the Mediterranean for foraging and growth, but confined to ever fewer beaches suitable for breeding.

There are no reports of *Chelonia* in the Adriatic *Caretta* over-wintering area and the importance of sites off south-east Turkey is unclear. Individuals are still being caught from the Gulf of Gabès during winter, where they feed on beds of sea-grass in the shallow warm sea - a habitat reported to be now mostly destroyed off Israel, Turkey and Egypt.

Very little information is known of their more general movements in the Mediterranean, partly because of their depleted numbers and because of the lack of tagging and their low susceptibility to being caught on long-lines.

Reasons for Decline and Current Threats

Direct Exploitation

Turtle-catching has much decreased since the late 1960s when the estimated Turkish catch was 6,000 per year. *Caretta* continues to be exploited by Malta, where markets sell 'live turtle meat' (steaks are reported to be hacked off tethered animals to order). This catching could be having a significant effect on the dwindling nesting stocks of Italy, Sardinia, Sicily and Lampedusa.

The worst problem is the annual exploitation of large numbers (estimated to be up to 5,000) of over-wintering turtles (mostly *Caretta*) in the Gulf of Gabès by the Tunisian fishing fleet following depletion of fish stocks because of over-fishing. Capture and slaughter of individual turtles in Egypt and the Middle East is still practised for folk-lore and pseudo-medicinal purposes, but the extent of this is not known.

Although illegal, it seems that fishermen in tourist areas are often tempted to take and even stockpile turtle shells for sale as souvenirs. The effects are likely to be localised but reports are regularly received of such exploitation from Crete, Tunisia, Turkey and Sardinia. Egg-collection continues locally in Turkey, was recently practised in Crete and may still occur in north Africa.

Incidental Capture

Large numbers of turtles are caught or killed as the incidental result of fishing activities. The turtle catch from long-line fishing (kilometres of heavy duty line with baited hooks at 10 metre intervals in the surface waters) off the Balearics alone has been estimated as up to 20,000 (predominantly immature) turtles per year. Some animals drown, while some others may be fatally injured after swallowing the hooks. Other fleets, including several from Asia, use similar methods in the Mediterranean and the cumulative effect of an annual mortality of between 3,000-12,000 maturing turtles is significant. This includes animals caught and drowned in set nets or by trawling - this can be disastrous if practised off nesting beaches or in feeding or over-wintering areas. No examples are known of the use of Turtle Exclusion Devices (TEDs) which would allow the escape of turtles from trawl nets. Additional disturbance to nesting areas is known to occur as a result of the localised (and largely unlawful) use of dynamite for fishing.

Pollution

This is an unquantified problem. Oil pollution is widespread and a fifth of the *Caretta* examined off Malta were found to have crude oil contamination of the mouth and gut. Turtle deaths have been associated with a chemical (suspected to be a pesticide) pollution incident in the north Adriatic in 1988. Heavy metal discharges seem certain to have had an adverse effect via the food chain, probably more so on *Caretta* than on the more herbivorous *Chelonia*. Loss or reduction of food as a result of effluent discharges along the coast may also be significant and some divers have reported the loss of sea-grass beds along stretches of the Israeli and Egyptian coasts as a result of pollution.

Untreated discharges from Turkish pulp mills are known to be biologically hazardous and yet these are a feature of several small rivers which divide turtle-nesting beaches and which now stain the sea offshore, for instance at Dalaman and Goksu. The important nesting beach of Kazanli straddles open discharges from two chemical factories which are causing serious heavy metal marine pollution. The effects of such pollution on hatchlings or nesting females resting offshore is not known.

Plastic wastes have also been shown to cause problems for turtles. *Caretta,* for example, ingest plastic cups (which may resemble squid or jellyfish in motion) and this could cause death. Piles of plastic wastes litter beaches in the triangle between Turkey, Cyprus and Syria which acts as a marine cul-de-sac trapping the discarded junk from ships and towns. Adult females have physical difficulties negotiating the beach over these shoreline barriers, and it is unlikely that hatchlings could successfully cross them to reach the sea.

Tourism

Many beaches used for nesting have been lost as a result of tourism development (Figure 13). Specific tourist-related activities which have reduced the suitability of breeding beaches include:

- removal of sand for building;
- photo-pollution from nearby hotels and tourist infrastructures;
- use of off-road vehicles over the nesting zones;
- use of bulldozers to clean the beach (this can destroy the natural beach profile and compact the sand as well as exposing nests);

- planting of shade trees such as pine and tamarisk may deleteriously affect the sand microclimate and damage eggs, as well as creating further obstructions;

- camping, barbecues, discos and other night-time beach uses create sufficient disturbance to prevent the females from nesting;

- increased predation from domestic dogs;

- increased use of small boats and storage of pedaloes creates obstacles for females and hatchlings;

- erection of sunbeds and umbrellas (the latter can pierce the nests and either can cool nests or obstruct adults and hatchlings);

- digging of pits and sand castles create lethal hazards for hatchlings;

- facing of the dune/beach interface with walls;

Figure 13: West Laganas beach in Greece, formerly an important turtle nesting site, has been totally lost to tourist development (photo: P. Vodden).

Physical disturbance, even from walking over the sand, may precipitate premature emergence from activated nests during daytime hours, with fatal consequences for hatchlings, which can perish within a few metres of their nests in the heat of the day.

Photo-pollution is often a cause of hatchling loss on some of the remaining Greek and Turkish breeding beaches (Figure 14). Instead of heading for the sea, the newly emerged hatchlings are enticed inland by the brighter light from houses, hotels, bars, street lights and cars. The hatchlings may survive until daylight but perish when daytime temperatures increase or predators locate them. This phenomenon is a universal problem of coastal development and one to which the turtles have no possible natural defence, as it results from their basic biological instinct of heading for the natural night-time light source - the sea (Figure 15).

The increasing use of shallow bays for small motor-powered boats, particularly for water-skiing and para-ascending is known to be a

Figure 14: The beginnings of tourism on a Turkish nesting beach. By locating the hotel on a promontory, the maximum photo-pollution effect has been assured (photo: K. Corbett).

problem. For instance, recent examination of turtles nesting at Zakynthos showed that almost half had injuries consistent with collisions with boats or from propeller impacts.

Conservation Measures Taken

As yet, there is not a single effectively protected nesting beach in the Mediterranean, nor has any dialogue been initiated with fisheries ministries to resolve the fishing problems.

International trade in marine turtles and their derivatives is banned under CITES, and turtles are theoretically protected under the Berne Convention by all maritime members of the CoE, except Malta which is not a party to the convention. The largest nesting population of *Caretta* at Zakynthos has been the subject of successive and detailed Recommendations under the Berne Convention (see Appendix 2) as well as two associated 'On-the-spot Appraisals'. Turkey has accepted one Recommendation not to allow completion

Figure 15: A hatchling Caretta caretta *makes for the luminosity of the open sea - unless diverted to disaster by the brighter lights of hotels and roads along the top of the beach (photo: R. Jesu).*

of a hotel development on the Dalyan nesting beach (Plate 10), as well as a further Recommendation to reconsider long-standing tourism development proposals in relation to the importance of various sites for nesting turtles.

Ecological research and education projects have been funded in Greece by the EEC and WWF, as has a project to educate fishermen in Italy and a recent turtle survey in Tunisia. Two nesting beach surveys, funded by the EEC and WWF, have recently been successfully completed for the south Turkish coast and eastern Cyprus. Research and tagging programmes on Zakynthos, Cephalonia and at Dalyan have further advanced knowledge of turtle dynamics and movements in the Mediterranean, and have confirmed population declines. Surveys have been carried out along parts of the south and west Peloponnese coast, on Crete and Rhodes, with some monitoring of relict Italian populations including those on Sicily and Lampedusa.

Presidential Decrees and associated Ministerial Decisions have been made for Laganas Bay on Zakynthos, mainly for development purposes. Although turtle conservation needs have been incorporated in these declarations, they are rarely implemented. There continues to be conflict with development, especially plans for a major increase of dwellings behind the important nesting beach at Kalamaki and Laganas (Figure 16).

Marine protection for the Gulf of Orosei was recently declared then suspended following an appeal from the Sardinian authorities. However, a CoE Recommendation has recently been passed urging that this area should be protected and it is hoped that this action may help deter further tourist encroachments.

Israel has protected marine turtles and has also carried out a modest hatchery programme since the early 1980s.

North Lara beach in western Cyprus has some measure of protection and a government research and hatchery programme is well established, although the gains from this project may be undermined by the uncontrolled tourist development of the Akamas peninsula which threatens both the Lara coast and other significant nesting beaches. Disturbance from tourists is already a problem on

Figure 16: Uncontrolled abuse of a critical stretch of beach at East Laganas Bay (Greece) leading to sand compaction, shading of nests and physcial obstruction of the turtles (photo: L. Veniselos).

parts of the nesting beaches at Lara and Toxeftra, but draft legislation to improve their protection is presently proceeding through the Cyprus Parliament.

Dalyan and North Calis beaches in Turkey have recently been protected under the provisions of the Barcelona Convention though it is not yet clear what practical measures may follow this initiative.

Conservation Measures Needed

The priorities are given below, many of which have been addressed by the Standing Committee of the Berne Convention (Appendices III, IV and V), with greatest urgency wherever *Chelonia* occurs:

- Protection of all important nesting beaches <u>and</u> their adjacent coastal waters.
- Overwintering sites off Turkey and Tunisia must be protected from fisheries pressures.
- Action is required by fishery authorities to reduce mortalities resulting from long-lining and to similarly reduce the number

of accidental catches of turtles.

- Nesting surveys and monitoring are required in North Africa, Sardinia, southern Italy, southern Crete and other potential Aegean sites.
- The overwintering area in the Adriatic requires more investigation and adequate protection.
- Artificial enhancement of hatching rates, especially of *Chelonia*, should be immediately undertaken, but should not include new captive rearing projects.
- Photo-pollution of nesting beaches needs to be reduced, for instance by re-locating and re-orienting the major sources of photo-pollution, and the shielding (for instance, by planting screens of trees inland) of other sources where possible.
- Pollution of the coastal waters in the vicinity of nesting beaches (particularly in Turkey) must be significantly reduced.
- Malta and Tunisia must prohibit the capture and sale of marine turtles.

Adequate protection of 20 beaches with 100-500 nests per year (40-200 females) could produce a potential hatch of up to one million eggs (at 100 eggs per nest). Such protection, together with the continued, if declining, recruitment from less important beaches, would thus give a chance of stabilising the decline of marine turtles in the Mediterranean, particularly of *Caretta*. However, stabilising the decline cannot succeed without a significant and concurrent reduction in mortality resulting from fisheries activity.

The following beaches and their marine surrounds are priorities for immediate and appropriate conservation measures:

Greece: Kiparissia, East Laganas/Kalamaki, Sakania, Dafni (Figure 17), together with any major nesting sites discovered in current surveys of the south Peloponnese.

Cyprus: Toxeftra*, Lara, Polis, Paleokastro*, East Karpas*.

Turkey: Dalyan, Dalaman, Fethiye/North Calis, Patara, East Kale, East Kumluca/Mavikent, Belek*, Nigit/Parakende, East Side*, West Kizilot, Demirtas, Gazipasa/

Cirtlik, Anamur, West Goksu, Kazanli*, Akyatan*, Samandagi*.

Italy: South Sicily, Lampedusa-Conigli, Sardinia-Orosei and any other nest sites located by survey.

Tunisia: Cap Serrat, Nabeul.

*Beaches also used by *Chelonia* and therefore of enhanced importance.

It should be noted that although the beaches of Italy and Tunisia hold only remnant nesting turtle populations, their protection may be important for the future of nesting in the western Mediterranean.

Figure 17: Dafni beach in Greece. This small stretch of Laganas Bay is partially protected and, like Sekania, is over-crowded with nests. The amount of destruction of old nests by females digging fresh ones is unknown, but the population continues to decline (photo: L. Veniselos).

By far the largest responsibility for turtle conservation falls on Turkey and it is therefore encouraging to note that the Turkish government has agreed to reconsider all current and future tourist development projects where important nesting sites may be threatened. Adequate field data now exists and application of conservation measures is now awaited.

In Greece, the appalling situation at Zakynthos and of the Mediterranean's largest nesting population of *Caretta* in Laganas Bay must be improved and adequate conservation measures implemented, including protection of the East Laganas and Kalamaki nesting areas, currently subject to deliberate damaging and illegal activities (Figures 16 and 18).

Figure 18: A heavy-duty metal sign encouraging turtle conservation vandalised by local land-owners at Zakynthos (photo: M. Schiavo).

IBIZA WALL LIZARD and LILFORD'S WALL LIZARD
Podarcis pityusensis and *Podarcis lilfordi*

Biology

Both *Podarcis pityusensis* (Plate 8) and *P. lilfordi* are medium-sized lacertid lizards ranging from 6-9cm head and body length, with *P. lilfordi* tending to the smaller range and having noticeably smaller scales. They are both noted for exhibiting a high degree of colour and pattern variation between populations, with the most pronounced differences being associated with the amount of isolation between the islands or islets where they occur (Plate 9). Their morphology is complex and illustrates the process of micro-evolution on small islands.

The adaptability of these lizards is reflected by the variety of habitats they occupy. The small islands or islets which support them present a wide spectrum of aspect, shape, size, vegetation cover and type (Figures 19 and 20), and in the degree of separation from each other and from their "mainlands" of Ibiza, Formentera, Mallorca and Menorca. The substrate may be rocky, or rock overlain with sand,

Figure 19: Example of rocky habitat occupied by Podarcis lilfordi
(photo: K. Corbett).

Figure 20: An example of hummocky turf occupied by Podarcis lilfordi
(photo: K. Corbett).

and the terrain ranging from cliff-like (rising a sheer 400m on Vedra), to flat areas near to high tide levels. Plant cover varies from bare rock through to mattoral and to woodland patches. The natural vegetation falls within the associations of *Crithmo-limonietum, Arthrocnemetum fruticosii,* or *Oleo-ceratonion.*

Their food choice appears to be catholic: besides taking most available invertebrates they will take their own young and those of the sympatric geckos (*Hemidactylus turcicus* and *Tarentola mauritanica*). They also scavenge (often along the sea shore), and may sometimes take a significant proportion of plant material, including nectar, in their diet.

Both species are egg-laying, with *P. lilfordi* laying smaller clutches. Both species bask and are diurnal in habit. Rock fissures may be important refuges against their many potential mammal and bird predators and this may also account for locally high population densities in sparsely vegetated areas.

Past and Present Distribution

The world distributions of the two lizards are contained within the area of the Balearic Islands, with *P. pityusensis* confined to the western "Pitiusas", including the two main islands of Ibiza and Formentera. *P. lilfordi* is confined to the eastern "Gimnesias", excluding the two main islands of Mallorca and Menorca. Within this range, *P. pityusensis* occupies 47 islands or islets, while *P. lilfordi* is found on 29. With the exception of Formentera and possibly of Ibiza, their populations tend to be low, from tens to low hundreds.

Until 1,500 years ago, *P. lilfordi* also lived on the main islands within its range, but the sub-fossil records show that it disappeared soon after the arrival of snakes in the Balearics. *P. pityusensis* still survives on its main islands, albeit in declining numbers and range, because the snakes do not include *Macroprotodon cucullatus*, a snake that feeds on lizards and which, significantly, inhabits both Mallorca and Menorca where *P. lilfordi* once occurred.

Reasons for Decline and Current Threats

Recent declines include the loss of the subspecies *P. l. rodriguez* because of the dynamiting of its island to improve navigation, the levelling of an Ibizan islet for the building of a hotel (to the detriment of *P. p. ratae*), several instances of causeway construction to connect islands to the mainland and the subsequent dilution and loss of subspecies by hybridisation, deliberate poisoning of populations, the use of islets (especially around the *P. lilfordi* stronghold of Cabrera) for naval target practice, tourism and visitor pressure, predation from domestic animals and collection. A question mark hangs over the future of the island of Espalmador inhabited by *P. pityusensis*, where tourist development is a continual threat and where nature reserve status has been proposed but not yet granted.

After the physical loss of habitat for tourism, the most significant threat is commercial collecting. For example, although illegal under Spanish national law and strictly controllable under the Berne Convention, the 1980s have seen the regular sale of wild-caught *P. pityusensis* in Germany, and the unlicensed collection for "research" of two subspecies of *P. lilfordi*. Random customs searches in the UK resulted in one suitcase found in 1986 that contained 500 *P. pityusensis* (420 died and 80 were returned to the Balearics) and another found in 1988 that contained 400 *P. pityusensis* (all returned). Another 2,000 *P. pityusensis* were impounded at Schiphol airport in

Holland in 1988. While any collection of the lizards can only have adverse effects on populations, the principal method adopted of sinking plastic buckets into the ground to act as pitfall traps is particularly destructive since these may be infrequently attended, or abandoned, and lizard mortality is predictably high. Measures are required to stamp out this practice.

Some hybridisation of otherwise discrete subspecies has recently become evident and has apparently occurred as fishermen have stocked islands nearer to their base with more attractive specimens collected from further out to sea. This allows greater ease of collection when demand dictates.

Conservation Measures Achieved

Both species are strictly protected under Spanish law. Excellent research work has been done by the Balearic government to locate, assess and type all their populations. However, actual site and habitat protection measures have been limited to:

-       local controls against urban and tourist development (particularly on the Es Freus group, inhabited by *P. pityusensis*);

-       the Cabrera group (supporting *P. lilfordi*) has been accepted for National Park status by the local Balearic government. However, its designation by the national government has been held up by objections from the army who had recently enlarged the garrison and who continue to shell the area;

-       development and a possible causeway to join Murada (with *P. pityusensis*) to the mainland appears to have been averted.

Conservation Measures Proposed

Maintaining the scientific value of these lizard populations for their zoo-geographical and evolutionary features requires preservation of the total genetic integrity of the two species. This implies adequate local measures under Balearic and Spanish national law to protect populations, sites, and their habitats. But, how many of these populations of localised endemics merit international measures such as Biogenetic Reserves? It would be logical and sensible to include the rarer, the more distinct, the most isolated (temporally and spatially) populations exhibiting a range of distinct subspecific characters. Fortunately the data do exist to guide this compromise and they have been used to recommend Biogenetic Reserves.

For *P. lilfordi,* all populations are eligible, in deference to their comparative rarity, lower total numbers and absence from the main islands. Aire Island, Colomer (proposed for inclusion within a Biogenetic Reserve for *Alytes muletensis*), and the Cabrera complex already justify Biogenetic Reserve status, and undoubtedly most if not all of the remaining ten islands and islets will merit similar status, following analysis of recent field and laboratory investigations by the Balearic government wildlife authority.

The situation is more problematical for the 41 or so subspecies of *P. pityusensis,* described from 47 island locations and including the comparatively large and widespread populations of *P. p. pityusensis* and *P. p. formentera,* found respectively on Ibiza and Formentera. However, a classification by Cirer of these many populations into seven main groups based on sea depth, post-glacial separations and detailed morphometrics is most valuable for Biogenetic Reserve assessment purposes, not least since five of her seven groups contain the most distinct and longest separated forms. Using this information, the following islands or groups of islands are justified for Biogenetic Reserve designation: Bledas, Espartas, Es Freus, Vedras, Margalida, Murada, Conileras and Cana.

Many of these islands support seabird colonies, notably of Audouin's gull (*Larus audouinii*) and some have Eleonora's falcon (*Falco eleonorae*). The management of the reserves must include precautions against collection, and must especially control landings by tourists or fishermen. Other potential conservation gains could be the local re-establishment of monk seals (*Monachus monachus*) and the protection of feeding areas for the endangered loggerhead turtle (*Caretta caretta*) from a modest degree of marine reserve buffer zones (including controls over fishing) around certain islands.

Rare and endemic plants are also found in these proposed reserves, including *Helichrysum lamarcki, Astragalus balearicus, Diplotaxis catholica ibicensis, Withania frutescens, Rhamnus ludovici-salvatoris, Medicago arborea citrina, Euphorbia margalidensis, Silene italica ifacensis* and *Carduncellus dianeus.*

ORSINI'S VIPER
Vipera ursinii ursinii

Biology

This viper closely resembles the meadow viper (*V. (u.) rakosiensis*) considered below, but has a grey to white ventral surface. It has quite restricted habitat requirements, most frequently found on sheltered south-facing slopes on calcareous substrates with a variable vegetation cover of grasses and low herbaceous plants, at altitudes from 1,400-2,400m above sea level. A typical feature of its habitat is *Juniperus communis nana* (dwarf juniper), although this may not be an essential habitat factor since the viper also occurs at a few sites which lack juniper. However, the best viper populations are generally found in areas with good juniper stands (Plate 13).

The vipers usually hibernate between October and March-April. Hibernation sites include rodent tunnels and crevices in the ground or under rocks, and are situated in the same general area that supports their spring and summer activity. They may be found basking from early morning until early afternoon during spring, but only bask for very brief periods during summer. Mating occurs between April and May. The young, typically three to eight in number, are born between the end of July and mid August. The viper feeds almost exclusively on arthropods, especially large flightless Orthopterans, the particular species taken varying at leach locality in the central Appennines.

Past and Present Distribution

Vipera ursinii comprises of a taxonomically complex group, with distinctive populations occurring at scattered localities ranging from Western Europe east to Western Asia, represented by small, isolated and often diminishing populations.

A major revision of the European vipers will be completed in 1990 and will lead to a number of significant changes in the classification of the *V. ursinii* group based on genetic, morphological and ecological characters. Already, the widespread, lowland population, until recently considered a subspecies of *V. ursinii,* has been separated and named *V. renardi* . It is clear that each regional population differs markedly and even individual montane populations merit conservation attention owing to their distinctiveness and geographical isolation. At the present time, the montane populations in France and Italy can be assigned to *V. u. ursinii*, those in Yugoslavia and Bulgaria to *V. u. macrops*, and those in Greece to a new taxon perhaps related to *V. u. macrops*. The taxa found in Turkey, *V. u. eriwanensis* and *V. u. anatolica* are quite separate from the other European forms and more closely resemble Middle East taxa. This chapter is concerned only with the CoE populations that are presently recognised as belonging to *V. u. ursinii*.

France

Nine small and isolated populations of *V. u. ursinii* are known in the south-east uplands in Vaucluse, Alpes de Haute-Provence and Alpes-Maritimes, notably at Mont Ventoux, Mont de Lure and Cheiron (Figure 21). The total population in France is considered seriously endangered and may number only 200 to 300 adults.

Figure 21: Habitat of Vipera u. ursinii *in isolated montane meadows with juniper scrub in southern France (photo: K. Grossenbacher).*

Figure 22: Montane habitat of Vipera u. ursinii *in the proposed Biogenetic Reserve of Gran Sasso, Italy (photo: B. Groombridge).*

Italy

V. u. ursinii is restricted to the central Appennines in the regions of Marche, Umbria and Abruzzo. Populations are known at Monti Sibillini, Monti della Laga, Gran Sasso, the Velino group and possibly within the Parco Nazionale d'Abruzzo. Total numbers are likely to be greater than in France, but it must still be regarded as threatened and at risk from collecting and habitat loss. Of the Italian sites, the Campo Imperatore area of the Gran Sasso appears to be the most important site for the species. This site is an inter-montane basin of around 1,660-1,750m elevation, showing glacial and karstic features, and supporting rich grazing pastures with scattered juniper mats (Figure 22). The basin extends for some 15-18km from west to east and is 2-4km wide. Its northern limit is formed by a continuous ridge of mountains around 2,500m high, extending eastward from Corno Grande (at 2,912m the highest peak in the Appennines, with the only surviving glacier). This entire northern ridge forms a slope 15km by 1km in extent, oriented to the south, and is prime habitat for *V. u. ursinii*. The area is also important for endemic or otherwise noteworthy plants, insects and birds.

Greece

The occurrence of *V. u. ursinii* in Greece was confirmed only in 1988. It appears to have several relatively healthy populations generally centred on montane meadows in the Pindos Mountains at around 2,000m. More fieldwork is required before any detailed conservation measures can be formulated.

Reasons for Decline and Current Threats

A major threat is collecting by animal dealers and by amateur and professional herpetologists. It is not difficult for a knowledgeable collector to remove very large numbers of vipers, and the numbers removed may represent a significant proportion of the local population. They are usually collected soon after emergence from hibernation, or while they bask early in the season. Habitat loss and disturbance resulting from winter tourist development and the mechanical preparation of pistes have adversely affected some populations, notably at Mont Ventoux in France. It appears that clearance of juniper by burning may be a significant threat, but no data are available on the extent of this practice.

Conservation Measures Achieved

V. u. ursinii is nominally protected in France by a decree of May 1979, under the Law of Nature Protection. Designation of protected areas has been discussed but apparently not yet implemented; the authorities relying on passive secrecy to avert potential collection. In Italy, the species has been reported within the Parco Nazionale d'Abruzzo, but this has not been confirmed in recent years. It is listed in Appendix II of the Berne Convention and also Appendix II of CITES.

Conservation Measures Proposed

The main conservation priority is that prime habitat for *V. u. ursinii* must be included in effectively managed protected areas. The Campo Imperatore area of the Gran Sasso in Italy (Plate 12) is the top priority for habitat protection measures in the CoE area. In addition, appropriate protection and management must be afforded to the best sites in France, while the status of *V. u. ursinii* in the Pindos Mountains needs further investigation.

MEADOW VIPER
Vipera (ursinii) rakosiensis

Biology

This is the smallest and least poisonous of the European vipers. It is typically less than 50cm long, and often has a rough appearance to the skin due to heavily keeled scales which may be so shortened that the dark skin shows between them. It sports the classic viperine dorsal zig-zag pattern, usually with a dark edging, and has a dark ventral surface. It is well known for its docility, seldom raising much more than a hiss when handled (Figure 23). Large invertebrates, especially crickets and grasshoppers, are prominent in its diet, but lizards (especially *Lacerta agilis*) and occasionally frogs and nestling rodents are also taken. Juvenile snakes have been observed feeding on *Gryllus campestris* and sheltering in their burrows. Late summer birth follows April mating, and from two to 20 young may result depending upon the size and age of the female. They may only breed in alternate years.

Figure 23: The critically endangered Vipera (ursinii) rakosiensis *is so harmless that it can be held in an ungloved hand. The unusual pattern on the right hand snake is confined to individuals from only two of the remaining Hungarian populations (photo: G. Nilson).*

This isolated subspecies is entirely restricted to lowland and occupies the more sandy habitats of alluvial meadows and 'puszta' in central Europe. Although best known from the damper summer meadows, it is clear that it utilises a combination from the very dry and sandy to those flower-rich meadows regularly inundated during winter; and within this range it would appear that the intermediate zone between wet and dry has a special ecological significance. To be used by *V. (u.) rakosiensis* wet and dry habitat must be found in close proximity, and perhaps ideally within the same area of meadow enhanced by low slopes and ridges (Plate 14). These *V. (u.) rakosiensis* localities also support rich and diverse communities of invertebrates, lizards and frogs.

The potential predators of the viper are legion and range from the uncommon great bustard (*Otis tarda*) to the abundant introduced pheasant (*Phasianus colchicus*).

Past and Present Distribution

The overall world range of *Vipera ursinii* is described in the previous section on *V. ursinii ursinii. V. (u.) rakosiensis* is a particularly distinct subspecies, restricted to a clearly defined and geographically limited habitat.

V. (u.) rakosiensis is among the most endangered reptiles in Europe. In Hungary, its last stronghold is in the Great Plain pusztas between the rivers Danube and Titza south of Budapest. Elsewhere, its habitat has been severely fragmented and is under pressure from modern agriculture and few of its localities have been protected. It has almost been lost from the Little Plain 'Hansag' where only one 12ha meadow is protected for *V. (u.) rakosiensis*. In Romania, it has recently become extinct following 'improvements' to its known meadow sites. In Austria, *V. (u.) rakosiensis* was most abundant in the sandy plains of the Vienna and Neusiedler basins until modern agriculture destroyed almost all of its habitat. The last sizeable population was lost in the 1970s, and the species is now considered to be near to extinction. There are however, three sites with remaining habitat and with persistent, though occasional, reports of the viper.

Reasons for Decline and Current Threats

The major single cause of decline in Austria has been land drainage and subsequent use for vineyards (Figure 24), arable farming (Figure 25) or forestry. Several secondary pressures have now become prominent at the last remaining sites, including the adverse effects on the meadows from direct or indirect application of fertilisers and pesticides, too frequent mechanical mowing which destroys the structure of the habitat (Figure 26) and can also kill and injure the snakes. Collection for museum and private use; rearing of game birds (especially in Austria) which heavily predate these small snakes and their young; and grazing and grubbing of some Hungarian pusztas by large herds of geese and pigs which degrade the habitat and cause direct predation. Killing for bounty was a significant local cause of decline, especially around Laxenburg (Austria) where annual kills running into thousands were recorded around the turn of the century.

Within its Austrian range the obvious reason for its continued decline in recent years has been a lack of interest and general complacency about the fate of both the snake and its meadow

Figure 24: The conversion of dry meadows to vineyards is a major threat to Vipera (ursinii) rakosiensis *in eastern Austria (photo: R. Podloucky).*

Figure 25: Arable reclamation of the puszta in Hungary leads to loss of habitat for Vipera (ursinii) rakosiensis *(photo: K. Corbett).*

Figure 26: This area of structurally diverse meadow in the Hansag is the last site for Vipera (ursinii) rakosiensis *in western Hungary (photo: K. Corbett).*

habitat, despite many published reports on its conservation plight. This has been most recently demonstrated by the non-implementation of the Berne Convention provisions. The largest area of 'conserved' meadow is in Burgenland covering over 500ha, yet only 17ha in small isolated fragments actually receive protection, and there is no enforcement whatsoever on the ban on ploughing or the controls on pesticide or fertiliser use. Although the snake itself is protected against collection, there is again no enforcement and the best known breeding population in the above meadows was extinguished by collectors in the 1970s.

Conservation Measures Achieved

Apart from nominal protection of the species in Austria, no habitat provisions exist, and this highly endangered snake therefore remains essentially not conserved in Europe. However, the adoption of a recommendation for the conservation of *V. (u.) rakosiensis* by the Standing Committee of the Berne Convention (Appendix I) has prompted a site meeting with the Austrian authorities and this may result at least in more detailed survey and sympathetic management of the site in Lower Austria.

Conservation Measures Proposed

In general, habitat protection is urgently needed, together with some local reversal of recent ploughing and growing of maize where this is directly adjacent to unimproved meadow. Pheasants should be be actively discouraged wherever there are recent records for *V. (u.) rakosiensis*, namely at the three sites detailed below.

In particular, the last extensive meadow area in Lower Austria should be fully protected with urgent implementation of an appropriate management plan to conserve and enhance the remaining habitats, together with a coordinated survey to assess the current status of *V. (u.) rakosiensis* . Of the two sites left in Burgenland, the first (Zitzmannsdorfer Wiesen) should be fully protected and the current illegal abuses controlled, and wherever possible reversed, by prompt action from the authorities. The second area is privately owned and secluded; its meadows should be protected and enhanced by appropriate management, for which prompt negotiations are needed.

All three sites would benefit from designation as Biogenetic Reserves in order to protect their internationally important habitats, their surviving populations of *V. (u.) rakosiensis* and other notable species, including such plants such as *Gentiana pneumonanthe*, *Chondrosoma fiducaria*, *Scolopendra cingulata*, invertebrates such as *Hogna singoriensis* and *Citellus citellus*, the great bustard, *Lacerta vivipara pannonica* (glacial relict lizard) and the rare *Sicista subtilis trizona* (southern birch mouse), which sometimes occurs.

If the *V. (u.) rakosiensis* population in any of these sites proves to be too low to allow natural recovery, a contingency plan for boosting the populations or even re-introducing the snake should be drawn up, with the necessary SEH and Austrian/Hungarian cooperation through captive breeding. Only the Lower Austria and the private Burgenland sites would seem to be suitable for this extreme measure, which hopefully will not be needed if the conservation recommendations are promptly adopted.

Although work on *V. (u.) rakosiensis* was chiefly directed at the CoE member state of Austria, there is increasing cooperation with the Hungarian government to carry out comparative ecological and conservation studies in Hungary. Protection has been improved at one site and assigned to a newly discovered locality. However, while surveys may identify other Hungarian sites, the future conservation of *V. (u.) rakosiensis* will depend upon gaining control of the management of the puszta meadows where it occurs, maintaining their structural diversity without harming the vipers themselves.

MILOS VIPER and MILOS WALL LIZARD
Vipera schweizeri and *Podarcis milensis milensis*

This section focuses on the herpetological conservation priorities in the Western Cyclades of Greece, with particular emphasis on the two species mentioned above.

Biology of *Vipera schweizeri*

This non-aggressive and oviparous viper reaches 65-75cm in body-length. The field survey carried out by SEH located individuals of *V. schweizeri* only in sheltered, densely vegetated valleys with rough, rocky slopes. Highest concentrations were noted along damp, rocky stream beds (Figure 27) typically fringed by a thick growth of *Nerium oleander, Pistacia lentiscus* and *Myrtus communis.* Valleys retaining some water throughout the summer were particularly well populated but for the most part the vipers were found along dry stream beds in late summer (Figure 28). Hillsides and valleys with reasonably well developed scrub communities dominated by *Juniperus phoenicea, Olea europea* and *Pistacia lentiscus,* particularly near water courses, also supported good numbers of *V. schweizeri.* At other times of the year, particularly in the spring breeding season, *V. schweizeri* was found away from water, on rocky, scrub-covered valley sides.

Much of the surface of Milos and nearly all of the other islands of the Western Cyclades inhabited by the vipers are covered by a typical degraded phrygana community of low, spiny bushes forming dense, impenetrable thickets interspersed with bare rocky ground. Extensive areas of such dry habitat hold very few or no snakes in summer but some individuals do occur where there are sufficient refuges provided by rock crevices, stone walls or patches of taller scrub. Parts of south-east Milos still hold a sizable viper population in such habitat, although most are typically found in gulleys and small, sheltered valleys. Snakes are absent from high ground, generally living below 300m and certainly not higher than 400m altitude.

Past and Present Distribution of *Vipera schweizeri*

V. schweizeri is confined to the Western Cyclades of Greece (Figure 29) on the islands of Milos, Kimolos, Polyaigos and Siphnos. Some

Figure 27: Summer habitat of Vipera schweizeri
(photo: D. Stubbs).

Figure 28: Vipera schweizeri *basking in the sun*
(photo: D. Stubbs).

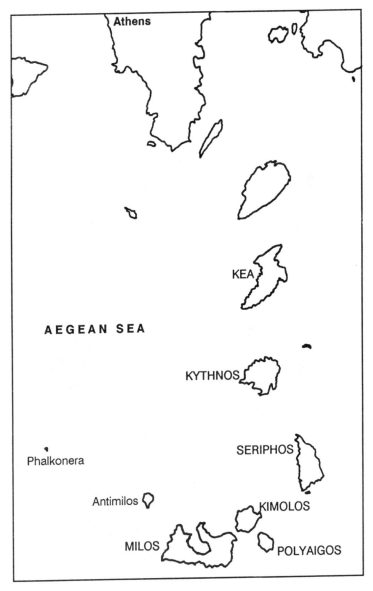

Figure 29: The Western Cyclades archipelago.

authors suggest it might also occur on Kythnos although most accept that this is very unlikely. The only island in the Milos group from which it is certainly absent is Antimilos.

A realistic present day population estimate would be in the order of 8,000-9,000 adult vipers (excluding Siphnos), of which about 90 per cent are on Milos. This gives an average density of one snake per hectare over all suitable habitat remaining on Milos today. Like most reptiles though, vipers have an uneven distribution and local densities vary greatly according to habitat differences. Distinct concentrations were found in certain valleys, and even along a single stream bed the vipers occurred in groups. An average of one viper per 100m at the best sites was usually derived from sightings of up to four individuals in one spot and several hundred metres without any sightings. Given the ease of overlooking well camouflaged individuals and the fact that in most snake species the majority of the population is inactive at any given time (even during normal activity periods) and therefore relatively undetectable, it is possible that as little as 10 per cent of the population is recorded at the best of times. On the basis of these few data there may be as many as one viper per 10-20m along suitable, undisturbed stream beds. However, it is not clear how much this is a seasonal effect, nor is it known from how large a catchment area the vipers are attracted. For these reasons it is important that any Biogenetic Reserve should have a substantial buffer area around each of the principal populations.

After Siphnos (not included in the survey), the next most populated island is Kimolos. This is, however, a very dry island with far fewer locations holding water in summer than Milos. Nevertheless, in these few localities there were good numbers of vipers. A large part of the island is high ground with very steep relief and short valleys. The total viper population may be little more than 100 individuals, or at most in the low hundreds.

Causes of Decline of and Current Threats to
Vipera schweizeri

Collecting

Although there is no documented evidence, collecting of *V. lebetina* for sale abroad has been going on for many years. It is not possible to state accurately how many are taken each year but the likely order of magnitude is between 1,000 and 1,500. Until 1977, a bounty system operated whereby people were paid a nominal sum (10 Drachmae, then worth about £0.15 or DM0.4) for each viper killed. Despite the lifting of the bounty system many animals continue to be slaughtered out of prejudice: many dead *V. schweizeri* were found during the survey, especially in eastern Milos. In latter years, though, live collecting has been increasingly prevalent and, for some local people, much more lucrative than the old bounties. A number of shepherds have been known to capture snakes during the course of their normal work and then sell them to foreign collectors. Most professional collectors come to Milos to do their own collecting and take relatively few vipers from shepherds. There are, however, certain well known rendezvous points where the vipers often still change hands. The collectors come from many different countries including the Federal Republic of Germany, Holland, Switzerland, Austria, Italy and Czechoslovakia. Again, precise numbers are not known but between 10 and 20 collectors probably come to the island each year, some of them twice a year. If they average about 50 snakes per visit, a fair assumption from anecdotal evidence, then around 1,000 individuals of *V. schweizeri* may be taken each year.

Lack of Law Enforcement

The 1981 Presidential Decree on wildlife protection outlawed the killing and collecting of most Greek reptile species including *V. schweizeri*. To date there have been no convictions despite the responsible authorities (the Forestry Service) being aware of certain offences. However, in September 1985, a German visitor who was about to leave Milos with 70 specimens of *V. lebetina*, was apprehended by SEH and the local police and all the snakes were confiscated and subsequently liberated back into the wild. It appears that charges were not pressed in this first ever case invoking Greek wildlife protection laws on the island, and nor was any action taken after a similar incident in 1986.

Mineral Extraction

There are several active quarries and mines on Milos, and one on Kimolos. The habitat destruction and disturbance at the opencast sites and along the access roads is posing a serious problem to the wildlife in eastern Milos (Figure 30). There are at present few active workings in west Milos, although there are numerous places where exploratory excavations have left their mark. Habitat recovery is minimal once the bedrock has been exposed.

Planning controls are practically non-existent so that new quarries can potentially spring up wherever valuable new deposits are located, and the mineral potential has caused the Greek government to oppose conservation measures. This has serious implication for landscape preservation and for all species of flora and fauna. Milos is noted as being one of the richest places in Greece for exploitable mineral resources and there are strong economic incentives for encouraging further development. Most operations, both actual and potential, are presently in the eastern half of Milos. Although there is likely to be some further exploitation of western sites, this is geologically the least interesting part of the island and should not be as heavily worked as in the east. However, in the future mining companies may well take a closer look at western Milos and neighbouring Kimolos and Polyaigos.

Figure 30: Extensive mineral exploitation on eastern Milos (Greece) that is now threatening to spread into a proposed reserve area for Vipera schweizeri *in western Milos (photo: G. van Mook).*

Tourism

Although tourism has greatly increased on Milos over the last ten years, it is not yet a major local industry. Tourist activity is also mostly confined to eastern Milos, mainly because of the present lack of infrastructure in the west. Kimolos and Polyaigos receive very few visitors. Currently, therefore, tourism does not appear to pose a serious threat to wildlife. However, if there is a programme to develop western Milos in the future, involving major road building and hotel and restaurant complexes, this would be a serious ecological problem, particularly for the snakes, which do not fare well near centres of human activity.

Biology of *Podarcis milensis*

This is a small (up to 65mm) insectivorous and egg-laying lizard, with a tendency to sexual dimorphism: males are brightly spotted, females more striped. Although its distribution is notably confined to a few islands, within this it would appear to have adapted to a wide variety of different habitats.

Past and Present Distribution of *Podarcis milensis*

This species is endemic to the Cyclades, being known only from Phalkonera in the far west of its range and the Milos group of islands (i.e. Milos, Kimolos, and Polyaigos). It is absent from Siphnos, where the indigenous small lacertid is *Podarcis erhardii*, a common species on many Aegean islands.

There are three described subspecies: *Podarcis milensis gerakuniae* (found only on Phalkonera); *Podarcis milensis schweizeri* (found only on Antimilos); and *Podarcis milensis milensis* (occurring on Milos, Kimolos and Polyaigos) which is the only subspecies dealt with here.

The highest frequency of sightings during the survey was noted in cultivated areas, along paths, stone walls and field edges. All potential habitats were occupied, although densities were apparently lower in remote and more natural areas. However this may only be a reflection of a more uniform availability of refuges and basking sites in contrast to the concentration of such features along field edges and paths in cultivated areas.

No published figures are available, nor is it realistic to estimate population size or density on the basis of this limited survey. The species is certainly abundant and must number many tens of thousands of adults.

Although the highest population densities found on Kimolos were associated with the abundance of stone walls, formerly cultivated ground and complex networks of mule tracks, there is an equally substantial population throughout the wilder area of western Milos. Large numbers of lizards were also seen on eastern Milos, again particularly around cultivated areas. Reduced predation pressure owing to the scarcity of snakes around farms and other habitations may be another factor influencing locally high lizard densities. However, on Polyaigos both lizards and snakes are rare. Lizards are largely restricted to the formerly cultivated areas of northern Polyaigos.

Conservation Measures Achieved

Both *Vipera schweizeri* and *Podarcis milensis* are protected on paper but laws prohibiting collection have been enforced only twice, and then with outside help. However, there is now official support for better enforcement of the collecting ban. There is no conservation of habitat or sites.

Conservation Measures Proposed

The Standing Committee of the Berne Convention has recognised that there is an urgent need for stronger protection of the Milos herpetofauna (Appendix I), particularly *V. schweizeri* and perhaps the rare *Elaphe situla* as well. Both species are highly threatened by a variety of factors and for the viper this is compounded by its very limited distribution. Populations of both species occur sympatrically with the endemic *P. milensis,* which although locally abundant, has a similarly restricted range. It is therefore essential that parts of the Western Cyclades are designated as a Biogenetic Reserve, that adequate measures are taken to ensure wildlife protection within these areas and that there are adequate buffer areas surrounding them.

Priority Area: Western Milos

The western half of Milos (about 8,000ha in extent) contains the largest concentrations of *V. schweizeri* in a wide range of its preferred habitats and this also includes the only known areas for the red colour variety of *V. schweizeri*. In this area there are also strong populations of most of the other reptile species occurring on Milos, and indeed all species of herpetofauna on the island are present within the proposed reserve area. It also incorporates two major nesting colonies of the rare Eleonora's falcon (*Falco eleonorae*) and the nesting area of Bonelli's eagle (*Hieraaetus fasciatus*) and possibly also Peregrine falcon (*Falco peregrinus*).

In terms of habitat, western Milos displays the least degraded examples of south Aegean phrygana and also holds remnant examples of the olive-carob evergreen woodland association (Plate 11). A full range of habitat types is represented, including perennially wet river valleys, dense scrub and open rocky psuedo-steppes, especially at high altitude. The Peak of Profitas Ilias has an important influence on the hydrology of much of western Milos. Although there are some good sites elsewhere on Milos, Kimolos and Polyaigos, there is no other possibility for designating a sizeable area of prime habitat for *V. schweizeri* as well as other typical flora and fauna.

Other Protected Areas

In addition to a Biogenetic Reserve on western Milos, it is important that some protection is granted to northern Kimolos and to all of Polyaigos. In terms of population densities of priority species neither area can be justified as a full Biogenetic Reserve. However, they both possess small and presumably stable populations of all the priority rated reptile species in the Western Cyclades with the possible exception of *Elaphe situla*. The current and potential human exploitation of both the smaller islands is low, so conservation measures should not cause significant conflict. It is important to note that neither area would in any way represent an adequate substitute for a Biogenetic Reserve in western Milos. Nevertheless, their conservation would help to ensure the integrity of *P. milensis* in its various island forms.

Enforcement of Wildlife Protection

Irrespective of the designation of reserve areas, there must be an immediate clamp-down on the snake collecting business throughout the Western Cyclades. Forestry Service officials and police on Milos must take positive action to halt all collectors visiting the island. At first this will be relatively simple since the collecting is still done quite openly. All that is required is for the local officials to be instructed to enforce the protection laws.

It is also essential that when caught all offenders are punished. Current penalties are totally inadequate as deterrents, especially in relation to the monetary value of the snakes, and stronger laws should be drawn up as soon as possible. Although the confiscation of all collected snakes is a severe loss to the collectors, there is currently no way of preventing them from coming back to collect more snakes another time. If current staffing levels on the island are insufficient for such enforcement, then an extra warden or a conservation officer should be employed specifically for wildlife protection.

Public Awareness and Education

Local attitudes towards wildlife in general and snakes in particular must be supportive of conservation if the designation of a Biogenetic Reserve is to have a positive effect. Initial prejudice against *V. schweizeri* generally turns to positive sympathy when people are informed of the ecological value and restricted range of a species. A local pride in the island's special rarities can be fostered and this will also help turn opinion against the foreign collectors.

With support from SEH, a poster depicting the snake and explaining in Greek the protected status and ecological and international importance of the species has been printed and displayed in all public places on Milos, Kimolos and Siphnos. It should also have German and English translations so that tourists are aware of the illegality of collecting. It is hoped that the poster will also serve to calm fears about the remote danger of snake bite as *V. schweizeri* is not an aggressive species, and a series of public lectures is reinforcing the message about reptile conservation.

Survey and Monitoring

It is understood that the designation of a Biogenetic Reserve carries with it a commitment to monitor wildlife populations within the reserve. In this respect a more detailed assessment of the population size and local distribution of *V. schweizeri* and possibly also *Elaphe situla* would be very valuable. This would help to identify all principal sites where development would be a serious threat and also to monitor the effect of the campaign against collectors. Detailed ecological information on *V. schweizeri* would also be of great scientific interest, and conservation of this largely bird-eating, egg-laying, non-aggressive and geographically isolated animal is essential and urgent.

5

Critical Species Assemblages in the Council of Europe Area

EAST SARDINIA, ITALY

Introduction

A study area in east Sardinia was chosen as the possible location of a Biogenetic Reserve, because of its high number of endemic species and wide variety of habitats within a relatively small area. The study attempted to assess the density and habitat selection of the herpetofauna and thereby to determine the most appropriate size and position of a reserve and to make recommendations for its adequate management.

Study Area

The area was located in the eastern part of the province of Nuoro. It was bordered by the Golfo di Orosei in the east, and ran from Orosei in the north to Baunei in the south, extending about 15km inland. It comprised mountainous country with plateaux, cliffs and some streams. The highest point, Monte su Nercone, was 1,263m above sea level.

Many superficial and subterranean cave systems were present, while at the river mouths in the east, there were sandy beaches, sand dunes, freshwater basins and marshy areas.

Herpetofauna

Of the 25 known species in Sardinia, 18 were present in the study area:

Tailed Amphibians:	2
Tailless Amphibians:	3
Tortoises and Turtles:	2
Lizards:	8
Snakes:	3

Among these were three endemic Sardinian taxa: *Speleomantes supramontis, Euproctus platycephalus* and *Natrix natrix cetti*, and six Tyrrhenian endemics: *Discoglossus sardus, Hyla sarda, Phyllodactylus europaeus, Algyroides fitzingeri, Podarcis tiliguerta* and *Podarcis sicula cetti*.

The following threatened taxa are listed according to the categories of threat assigned by the SEH (see Chapter 2):

Category 1:	*Caretta caretta*
Category 2:	*Speleomantes supramontis, Phyllodactylus europaeus, Natrix natrix cetti*
Category 3:	*Euproctus platycephalus, Discoglossus sardus, Emys orbicularis*

The most important species which appeared to be absent from the study area was *Lacerta bedriagae*, a Tyrrhenian endemic, and very rare on Sardinia. The absence of tortoises (*Testudo* species) was remarkable. *Coluber hippocrepis* survived only in the south-west of Sardinia.

Other Fauna

As well as the amphibians and reptiles, a number of other important animals occurred in the study area. Mammals include mouflon (*Ovis musimon*), wild cat (*Felis sylvestris*), wild pig (*Sus scrofa meridionalis*) and monk seal (*Monachus monachus*). Birds of prey include black vulture (*Aegypius monachus*), griffon vulture (*Gyps fulvus*), bearded vulture (*Gypaetus barbatus*) and Eleonora's falcon

(*Falco eleonorae*). The Tyrrhenian swallow-tailed butterfly (*Papilio hospiton*) was also present.

Habitats

The area may be divided into the following ten types of habitat:

Coastland

A complex of sandy beaches, sand dunes and freshwater pools in the coastal zone. The vegetation was characterised by sea holly (*Eryngium maritimum*), tamarisk (*Tamarix gallica*) and stone pine (*Pinus pinea*) in successive zones. In or adjacent to this dune area there were occasional freshwater pools ('stagnos'), influenced by the sea. The associated vegetation consisted of rushes (*Juncus* species) and glasswort (*Salicornia* species). *Podarcis sicula cetti*, *Chalcides ocellatus* and *C. chalcides vittatus* were abundant in this habitat. *Hyla sarda*, *Hemidactylus turcicus*, *Coluber viridiflavus* and *Natrix maura* were common. *Podarcis tiliguerta* was quite scarce and *Bufo viridis* rare. *Caretta caretta* have been reported from the beaches and offshore waters, but their breeding status was not investigated during the study.

Rivers and Streams

Streams traversed most of the other habitat types. Consequently, the bank vegetation was diverse, with several locally dominant plant species including bramble (*Rubus* species), cistus (*Cistus* species), tree heath (*Erica arborea*), oleander (*Nerium oleander*) and alder (*Alnus glutinosa*). During the summer, many of the smaller streams dried up. The most abundant reptiles and amphibians were *Podarcis tiliguerta*, *Chalcides ocellatus*, *Natrix maura* and *Hyla arborea sarda*. *Discoglossus sardus*, *Bufo viridis* and *Algyroides fitzingeri* were common. *Emys orbicularis* was rare and *Euproctus platycephalus* very rare.

Mountain Lakes

Only one lake exists in the study area, situated near Gola de Gorropu. This was probably dependent on over-flooding of the Rio Flumineddu, as well as precipitation. It appeared to be the most important habitat for *Euproctus platycephalus* in the area as a large population was found in the still water. The only other amphibian present was *Hyla sarda. Natrix cetti* occurred here in one of its only two localities in the study area.

Maquis

Maquis was a successional stage of holm oak (*Quercus ilex*) forest, usually maintained by grazing and burning. Two different types of maquis can be distinguished, known simply as 'low' and 'high'. Low maquis, which was generally less than a metre in height, was a first regenerative stage to forest of abandoned agricultural land. It can also be a degenerative stage of high maquis after fire. In the study area, dominant plants of low maquis included rosemary (*Rosmarinus officinalis*), cistus, mastic tree (*Pistacia lentiscus*), strawberry tree (*Arbutus unedo*) and phillyrea (*Phillyrea angustifolia*). The high maquis, which reached a height of 3-5m, was dominated by tree heath, strawberry tree and mastic tree. In low and high maquis, *Podarcis tiliguerta* and *Algyroides fitzingeri* were abundant species and *Coluber viridiflavus* was common, but the two skink species were rare.

Oak Forests

Holm oak dominated this habitat type. Other common tree species included cork oak (*Quercus suber*), mastic tree and strawberry tree. On a north-facing slope, where the soil was overlain by moss-covered rocks, a high density of *Speleomantes supramontis* was found. Reptiles were only present around the forest edges or in glades and included *Coluber viridiflavus, Podarcis tiliguerta, Algyroides fitzingeri* and once, *Natrix natrix cetti.*

Bare Rocks

A number of geological formations were exposed, including limestone and granite, dolomite and other volcanic rocks. Vegetation cover was scarce or absent, with holm oak, junipers (*Juniperus* species), cistus and rosemary comprising most of the vegetation, covering less than 5 per cent of the surface. *Hemidactylus turcicus* and *Phyllodactylus europeaus* were abundant in this habitat, as were *Algyroides fitzingeri* and *Podarcis tiliguerta. Coluber viridiflavus* was common but *Chalcides ocellatus* rare.

Caves

All caves were formed exclusively in limestone areas. Their depth varied from a few to several hundred metres, entrances varying from a few centimetres to some tens of metres. The caves were the favoured habitat of *Speleomantes supramontis* (Figures 31 and 32), although their numbers might be locally higher in moist oak forest. No other amphibians or reptiles were found here during the study.

Agricultural Areas

These included fields, pastures, orchards, vineyards and man-made pools, normally bordered by loose stone walls. The vegetation consisted of ruderal herbs, prickly pear (*Opuntia ficus-indica*), mastic tree and crops such as fig (*Ficus carica*), olive (*Olea europaea*) and vines (*Vitis vinifera*). These areas were very rich in both species and numbers of amphibians and reptiles. *Hyla sarda, Hemidactylus turcicus, Podarcis tiliguerta, P. sicula cetti, Chalcides ocellatus, C. c. vittatus* and *Coluber viridiflavus* were all abundant, *Bufo viridis* and *Natrix maura* were common, and *Phyllodactylus europeaus* rare.

Villages

These consisted of small settlements with scattered low buildings and comprise Orosei, Dorgali, Cala Gonone, Urzulei, Baunei and Santa Maria Navarrese. These were rich in species, but generally supported them in low numbers. *Podarcis sicula cetti* was abundant and *Hyla sarda* and *Hemidactylus turcicus* were common. *Discoglossus sardus, Tarentola mauritanica* and *Phyllodactylus europeaus* were rare, while *Bufo viridis, Podarcis tiliguerta* and *Natrix maura* were seldom seen.

Sea

The habitat of the marine turtles. Although none were seen during the study, local fishermen reported that they often caught loggerhead turtles close to the coastline, particularly near Orosei beach. However, no nesting survey was attempted.

Figure 31: Habitat of one of Sardinia's endemic cave salamanders,
Speleomantes supramontis, *at Orosei (photo: A. Stumpel).*

Figure 32: Speleomantes supramontis *in a crevice in
the above cave (photo: A. Stumpel).*

Threats

Although the study area was relatively undisturbed, man-induced changes were rapidly increasing and influenced both the density and diversity of the herpetofauna in a negative way. Six major problems exist, as itemised below.

Tourism

Many people were attracted to the area's hotels, restaurants, yacht harbours and watersport facilities, and there is increasing tourist transport to the previously undisturbed coast. Tourists caused significant disturbance, especially on the beaches, cliffs and in the maquis forests, where there is now a higher fire risk. Speleologists jeopardize the habitats of the cave salamanders by removing shrubs from concealed cave entrances which could lead to the adverse changes in the cave environment.

Agriculture and Forestry

Livestock numbers were increasing in the area, resulting in over-grazing and erosion. The maquis and forests were deliberately burnt by shepherds as well as accidentally. The holm oak forests were being cut on a large scale and replaced by pine plantations.

Infrastructure

The construction of roads and harbours was opening up and frag-menting the area and was allowing people, especially hunters, to obtain easy access to formerly remote places.

Commercial Collecting

The capture and trade of animals, including amphibians and rep-tiles, could lead to the extermination of some species. There was some evidence that the marine turtles were locally exploited.

Pollution

The use of toxic chemicals, and the dumping of waste products was of concern.

The Proposed Biogenetic Reserve

The borders of the proposed reserve are shown in Figure 33. The reserve would include both terrestrial and marine zones (Figure 34). The terrestrial section covers about 37,000ha. The eastern border follows the coastline, the northern was near Orosei, the southern was near Santa Maria Navarrese, and to the west the area extends about 5 kilometres west of the SS125 (Dorgali-Baunei) road.

Recommendations for the Management of the Biogenetic Reserve

In order to maintain the herpetofauna at least at its present density and diversity of species, a number of steps are necessary.

- Promoting conservation awareness among local inhabitants (villagers and shepherds), as well as local and regional authorities.

- Tourism should be controlled to reduce its negative impacts. For example, the new road in the south should be closed, the use of the new harbours near Caletta di Osalla and Orosei should be carefully supervised and picnics within the reserve should take place only at authorised sites. This implies the employment of wardens or rangers.

- Preservation of the traditional small-scale agriculture in and around Dorgali. Ways of achieving this without harming the livelihoods of local people need to be fully investigated to maintain the current balance of management inputs.

- The maquis and forest should be managed to avoid clearance, burning, unchecked grazing and disturbance by pigs.

- The old oak forests should be protected from exploitation and replacement by pine plantation.

- Caves inhabited by cave salamanders should be rendered inaccessible to people and domestic animals.

- Hunting and fishing by non-residents should be prohibited or strictly controlled.

- The use of insecticides and the dumping of harmful wastes

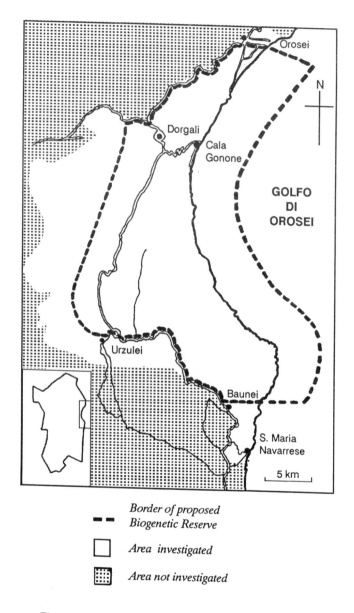

Figure 33: Boundary of the Proposed Biogenetic Reserve at Golfo di Orosei, Sardinia.

should be banned.

■ The collection and trade of amphibians and reptiles, especially the rare and endemic species should be prevented.

Figure 34: The proposed Biogenetic Reserve at Golfo di Orosei has a striking succession of habitats from the beaches with Eryngium *stands, through maquis to montane pastures (photo: A. Stumpel).*

EVROS, GREECE

Introduction

The southern part of the Greek province of Evros contains a number of natural areas belonging to the richest and most varied ecosystems of Europe, and reptiles and amphibians are well-represented there. In 1980 two small reserves were established within the area: one in the Dadia-Lefkimi-Souflion forest complex and one in the Evros delta. Alarming news concerning potential threats to these reserves led to investigations on the occurrence and the habitat selection of amphibians and reptiles in southern Evros. For the conservation of the herpetofauna it was considered to be very important to propose relevant parts of this area as a Biogenetic Reserve.

Study Area

The study area covered the southern part of the province of Evros, bordered in the west by the province of Rodopi, in the south by the Mediterranean and in the east by Turkey. The northern border ran between the villages of Mandra and Gonikon. The total area was approximately 2,000km² (40 x 50km), and because of military supervision was not freely accessible. The elevation of the area ranges from sea level (Evros delta) to 1,044m in the Sapka mountains in the north-west.

Herpetofauna

A total of 39 species was found in the study area:

Tailed Amphibians:	3
Tailless Amphibians:	9
Tortoises and Turtles:	4
Lizards:	11
Snakes:	12

Such a rich herpetofauna is now very unusual in Europe. Moreover, many of the amphibians and reptiles occur at very high densities, occupying a key position in the ecosystem as food for many raptors and mammals (Figure 35).

Figure 35: Tortoise carapaces assembled from below just one eagle nest, one of the many predators dependent on the abundance of reptile food (photo: P. Scholte).

The following threatened taxa are arranged according to categories of threat assigned by the SEH (see Chapter 2):

Category 2:   *Bombina bombina*

Category 3:   *Testudo hermanni, Testudo graeca, Emys orbicularis, Coluber caspius, Coluber najadum, Vipera xanthina*

Other Fauna

The area was inhabited by many birds of prey, especially in the old open oak and pine forests in the low mountains. These included golden eagle (*Aquila chrysaetos*), lesser spotted eagle (*A. pomarina*), short-toed eagle (*Circaetus gallicus*) and eagle owl (*Bubo bubo*). Many of them hunted in the surrounding cultivated areas or in the delta. The transition zone between mountains and lowland was used for very small-scale cultivation and supported a wide variety of passerine birds. The Evros delta itself, though mostly cultivated, is still of great importance for birds: more than 250 species were seen there during the study.

Some large carnivorous mammals were present in good numbers in the area, including wolf (*Canis lupus*), otter (*Lutra lutra*) and beech marten (*Martes foina*). Other interesting mammals were jackal (*Canis aureus*), marbled polecat (*Vormela peregusna*) and suslik (*Spermophilus citellus*), although they have declined considerably.

Habitats

Marshes and Riverine Forests in the Evros Delta

Along both sides of the shallow Evros river there were remnants of high riverine forests and marshy grasslands. By the coast, tamarisk stands, reedswamp and rushy marshland were present. Eighteen species occurred, notably *Bombina bombina, Pelobates syriacus, Testudo graeca, Emys orbicularis, Mauremys caspica, Coluber caspius* and *Elaphe quatuorlineata*. Seven species occurred in very high densities: *Bombina bombina, Pelobates syriacus, Bufo viridis, Hyla arborea, Rana ridibunda, Coluber caspius* and *Natrix natrix*.

Traditionally Managed Agricultural Land

This habitat type predominated around villages and consisted of small-scale arable plots, kitchen gardens, vineyards, wells and orchards, surrounded by hedges and coppice strips (Figure 36). The herpetofauna comprised 27 species, notably *Testudo hermanni, Testudo graeca, Emys orbicularis, Mauremys caspica, Ophisops elegans, Lacerta trilineata, Coluber caspius, Coluber najadum, Elaphe situla, E. quatuorlineata, Telescopus fallax* and *Vipera xanthina*. Some species occurred in very high densities, including *Testudo hermanni, Mauremys caspica, Cyrtopodion kotschyi, Lacerta trilineata,* and *Ophisaurus apodus*

Dehesa

This was a zone of agricultural land and open vegetation in foothills. It was characterised by a patchwork of small-scale but intensively

*Figure 36: The diverse landscape of traditional farming
in the Evros area (photo: H. Strijbosch).*

used arable land, vast cornfields and open pastures, and supported 30 species of reptiles and amphibians, notably *Bombina bombina, Testudo hermanni, Testudo graeca, Emys orbicularis, Mauremys caspica, Ophisops elegans, Lacerta trilineata, Ablepharus kitaibelii, Coluber caspius, Coluber najadum, Elaphe situla, Elaphe quatuorlineata, Telescopus fallax,* and *Vipera xanthina*. Four species occurred in very high densities: *Rana ridibunda, Testudo hermanni, Mauremys caspica* and *Cyrtopodion kotschyi*.

Old Native Pine Forest

This habitat type comprised a network of mountain ranges and valleys, and their branches, with open and closed pine *(Pinus brutia)* forests, bare rocky fields, pastures and deciduous shrubs. The herpetofauna consisted of 27 species, notably *Testudo hermanni, Testudo graeca, Emys orbicularis, Mauremys caspica, Lacerta trilineata, Ablepharus kitaibelii, Coluber caspius, Coluber najadum,* and *Telescopus fallax*. Nine species occurred in very high densities: *Bufo bufo, Rana ridibunda, Testudo graeca, Emys orbicularis, Ophisops elegans, Lacerta trilineata, Ablepharus kitaibelii, Natrix tessellata* and *Vipera ammodytes*.

Deciduous Woodland and Maquis

This habitat, found in the southern mountains, comprised a mixture of young holm oak (*Quercus ilex*) woods with a poorly developed undergrowth, and impenetrable maquis up to 5m high dominated by strawberry tree (*Arbutus andrachne*). Stands of plane (*Platanus orientalis*) grew in steep valleys and on cliffs. The herpetofauna numbered 23 species, notably *Testudo hermanni, Testudo graeca, Emys orbicularis, Mauremys caspica, Ophisops elegans, Lacerta trilineata, Coluber caspius, Coluber najadum, Elaphe quatuorlineata* and *Telescopus fallax*. *Testudo graeca, Emys orbicularis, Mauremys caspica*, and *Natrix tessellata* occurred in very high densities. It was difficult to establish the densities for other species because of the inaccessibility of the habitat.

Oak Parkland Forests in the Uplands (Pomak Country)

This complex of open oak (*Quercus* species) forests, grazed areas and brooks (Plate 15) consisted of old twisted trees with a total crown density of less than 50 per cent, and a poorly developed shrub layer (in contrast to the herb layer where *Cistus incanus* could cover more than 50 per cent of the ground surface). The herpetofauna consisted of 24 species, notably *Testudo hermanni, Testudo graeca, Emys orbicularis, Mauremys caspica, Ophisops elegans, Lacerta trilineata, Podarcis erhardii, Ablepharus kitaibelii, Coluber caspius* and *Coluber najadum*. Thirteen species occurred in very high densities: *Salamandra salamandra, Triturus vulgaris, Bombina variegata, Podarcis erhardii riveti, P. taurica, P. muralis, Lacerta viridis, Ablepharus kitaibelii, Ophiomorus punctatissimus, Malpolon monspessulanus, Coluber najadum* and *Natrix tessellata*.

Tall Deciduous Forests in the High Mountains

This habitat comprised closed forests with beech (*Fagus moesiaca*), hornbeam (*Carpinus betulus*) on both south and north-facing slopes, which were managed only at a very low intensity by selective felling of trees. Twenty-four herpetofauna species were recorded, notably *Rana graeca, Testudo hermanni, Testudo graeca, Emys orbicularis, Mauremys caspica, Lacerta praticola, Podarcis erhardii, Ablepharus kitaibelii* and *Coluber caspius*. Four species occurred in very high densities: *Salamandra salamandra, Bombina variegata, Rana graeca* and *Podarcis erhardii riveti*.

Threats

During the last few decades the natural quality of the area has diminished, particularly as a result of forest clearance and intensification of agriculture, both of which have increased the accessibility of the area.

Habitat Destruction

Intensive forestry is the biggest threat. Since 1974, native pine and oak forests have been cleared and replaced by dense Corsican pine (*Pinus nigra*) plantations, accompanied by the construction of access roads and the destruction of other natural and semi-natural vegetation. Agricultural intensification has involved drainage of wetlands in river valleys, and the loss of hedgerows and coppice strips. The use of agricultural machinery in the rich transition zone between natural habitats and agricultural land has caused massive casualties in tortoises, snakes and lizards. Much of the delta has now been reclaimed for agriculture and this has involved the clearance of riverine forests with consequent drying out of wetlands.

A further damaging change to herpetofauna habitats has been the migration of labour away from remote areas, with a consequent decrease in the number of goat herds in the low mountains. This was resulting in the loss of open grazed areas, which when interspersed with forest and other semi-natural habitats, provided optimal herpetofauna habitat in the past. Fire (deliberate and accidental) has been an additional pressure on herpetofauna habitats.

Persecution

Poaching of tortoises is thought to be significant. Undoubtedly, snakes and lizards are killed and persecuted but the degree of killing and its impact on individual species is not known.

The Proposed Biogenetic Reserve

The boundaries of the proposed reserve (Figure 37) were determined on the basis of the following criteria:

- The reserve must hold viable populations of threatened species, and sufficient habitat which is appropriately managed to ensure their conservation.

- The reserve must contain those biotopes characterized by an exceptionally high diversity and/or density of amphibians and reptiles.

- The reserve must hold viable populations of the rare birds and mammals that are present.

The total size of the proposed Biogenetic Reserve is 123,190ha, comprising:

- 10,960ha of mud banks, saltmarshes, coastal lakes, freshwater marshes, and riverine forests in the delta.

- 8,100ha of traditionally managed, small-scale agricultural areas.

- 31,920ha of dehesa buffer zone.

- 17,240ha of oak maquis vegetation, valleys with plane trees and steep cliffs.

- 21,610ha of native pine forest patches in the low mountains and hills.

- 18,800ha of open, grassy oak forests.

- 14,560ha of dense mixed deciduous forests in the high mountains.

Recommendations for the Management of the Biogenetic Reserve

In order to maintain, protect and increase the density and diversity of the herpetofauna, the following steps must be taken:

- Prohibition of further afforestation.

- Prevention of further agricultural intensification.

- The cessation of road building and the blocking up of some recently constructed roads.

- Protection of remaining wetlands from land drainage and

1. A male fire-bellied toad *Bombina bombina* calling from the surface of a densely vegetated lowland pond, its characteristic habitat. (C. Andren)

2. The prominent eyes of the Majorcan midwife toad *Alytes mulentensis* have envolved to cope with a life led in deep gorges and rock fissures. (R. Podloucky)

3.   Typical breeding site for the Majorcan midwife toad *Alytes muletensis*: in shaded pools replenished by the seasonal torrents it is safe from predation and competition by introduced snakes and frogs. (J. Myol)

4. A pair of Italian agile frogs *Rana latastei* in nuptial embrace. (K. Grossenbacher)

5. This stand of riverine forest at Bosco de Fontana, one of the most important remaining in the Po Valley of northern Italy, provides habitat for the Italian agile frog and has been proposed as a Biogenetic Reserve. (K. Grossenbacher)

6. Even where ponds still exist on arable farmland, the virtual lack of terrestrial habitat and the affects of fertilizer and pesticide run-off mean that their value for European amphibians is negligible. (C. Andren)

7. One of the most striking species of European herpetofauna, the attractive Eyed Lizard (*Lacerta lepida*) remains unprotected and is declining within Spain, its main distribution area. (E. Hosking)

8. Vedra, a striking islet lying off the south-west tip of Ibiza (Spain), supports a handsome subspecies of the Ibizan wall lizard *Podarcis pityusensis vedrae* as well as the rare Eleonora's falcon *Falco eleonorae* and Audouin's gull *Larus audouinii*. It has been proposed as a Biogenetic Reserve. (R. Podloucky)

9. The Vedran subspecies of Ibizan wall lizard *Podarcis pityusensis vedrae* is most beautiful and highly sought after by collectors. (I.C.O.N.A.)

10.   Dalyan beach in south-west Turkey is one of the most important nesting sites in the
Mediterranean for the loggerhead turtle *Caretta caretta*. (K. Corbett)
(a) Tourist development was prevented by the government only after the foundations for a
hotel had been laid.
(b) Behind the beach is a richly vegetated delta.

11.   Western Milos (Cyclades Islands, Greece) is clothed with extensive areas of relatively undisturbed maquis vegetation that supports the very rare endemic Milos viper *Vipera scheizeri* and the more abundant endemic Milos wall lizard *Podarcis milensis*. However, the maquis (a critical habitat) is threatened with destruction by uncontrolled expansion of open-cast mining. (D. Stubbs)

12.   This montane meadow is situated at about 1800 metres elevation at Gran Sasso in Italy. It is a critical habitat for Orsini's viper *Vipera ursinii ursinii* and has been proposed as a Biogenetic Reserve. (B. Groombridge)

13. Orsini's viper *Vipera ursinii* in its refuge of dwarf juniper *Juniperus communis nana* vegetation. (B. Groombridge)

14. This example of habitat structure for the meadow viper *Vipera (ursinii) rakosiensis* has tussocky grass and ant-hills that will disappear if frequent mechanised mowing is continued. (K. Corbett)

15. Assemblage habitat at Evros, north-east Greece, where the glades and woodland structure, including the "Pomak" country, has been maintained for over 2000 years by traditional shepherding, is now threatened by agricultural improvements and afforestation. (H. Strijbosch)

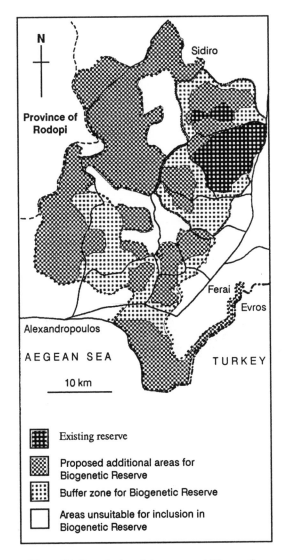

*Figure 37: Boundaries of the proposed Biogenetic
Reserve in the Evros Delta, Greece*

reduction of their water supply.

- Prohibition of hunting by other than local people.

- Appointment of guards.

- Promotion of selection forestry with felling intervals of not less than 100 years (pines) to 200 years (deciduous trees) in the wooded mountains, and the removal of wood with the help of mules.

- Encourage and manage a local increase of goat flocks in the low mountains at appropriate stocking levels.

- Provision of interpretive and educational facilities for tourists.

- Installation of a reserve centre for research, interpretation and reserve management purposes.

6
Further Work Required on Critical Species and Species Assemblages

The projects described in this chapter were confined to Council of Europe member states, and only to projects which could be completed during the short period 1983-1985 with the limited resources then available. Even so, it is felt that the projects were generally successful and have made a sound start to herpetofauna conservation in Europe and form a base on which a strategy for the whole continent can be developed in due course.

It is fair to say that whereas the research and survey work was swiftly completed, the translation of the results into practical conservation was seriously delayed, principally because of objections from two governments. The end product finally emerged in December 1988 as a formal Recommendation of the Council of Europe, and this is reproduced in full here as Appendix I.

The next step will be the actual implementation of the Recommendation. Meanwhile, there is a need to identify other urgent conservation priorities for reptiles and amphibians that were not covered in the project for the Council of Europe. Many of these concern species and species assemblages in Eastern Europe and Turkey. The SEH has identified the species listed on the next page as the top priority for further investigations.

*Salamandra (atra) aurorae**
Mertensiella caucasia
Mertensiella luschani
Chioglossa lusitanica
Triturus vittatus
Speleomantes ambrosii
Speleomantes flavus
Speleomantes genei
Speleomantes imperialis
Speleomantes supramontis
*Proteus anguinus**

*Rana holtzi**

Testudo hermanni hermanni (previously *robertmertensis*)
      in its south-west range
Testudo marginata
Trionyx euphraticus
Trionyx triunguis

Phyllodactylus europeaus
Chamaeleo chamaeleon
Lacerta bedriagae
Lacerta horvathi
Varanus griseus

Coluber cyprensis
Natrix natrix corsa
Natrix natrix cetti
Vipera barani
*Vipera kaznakovi**
Vipera (ursinii) renardi and aff. *renardi/rakosiensis*
      in Romania
*Vipera wagneri**

Table 3: Species of high priority for further investigation.
* Indicates the most urgent priorities.

The SEH has identified the following as the highest priority areas for further work to identify key species assemblies:

Greece:
the Peloponnese, with 45 species including five endemics.

Hungary:
puszta habitats between the rivers Danube and Tisza, with 24 species including a noted species assemblage.

Turkey:
at least three different regions (Adana area; north-east area towards the Soviet Union; and the south-east area towards Syria) have discrete assemblages of species not found elsewhere in Europe and supporting a number of endemics.

Yugoslavia:
the mountainous coast of the north-west supports a variety of reptiles (perhaps as many as 47 species) including a number of regional endemics.

Part Three

Country Accounts

7
Introduction

The accounts of the status of reptiles and amphibians in this part of the book focus on the conservation needs of species threatened at a national level. They are based on the experience of SEH members, national experts, and from the responses received to an international questionnaire circulated by SEH. This questionnaire sought information on the state of national and regional surveys, Red Data listings and the main threats, legislation, and conservation measures achieved and needed. Although great effort has been made to standardise the accounts for ease of reference, it is inevitable that with a large number of contributors, language difficulties, disparate levels of knowledge, and widely varied diversity of species in each country, this has not always been possible to achieve.

It should be said that the conservation measures proposed to tackle the priorities identified are themselves liable to change in line with ever increasing rates of agricultural and urban development, although they are based on information available up to March 1989. Nevertheless, the proposals made to address these issues will alleviate, if not reverse, the general decline of reptile and amphibian populations, and the loss of their habitats. The greatest changes in knowledge are likely to occur in Yugoslavia, Greece and Turkey as fieldwork there progresses. In addition, many countries are in the process of drafting new legislation covering reptiles and amphibians and/or their habitats.

A number of subspecies are mentioned in the national accounts that are not included in the European checklist given in Part One. National experts consider that these taxa need conservation attention, and their inclusion here is further justified by the requirement of the Berne Convention to safeguard 'local races'. In each country, however, the highest priority must be accorded to species of international importance, and this has been stressed in the text wherever appropriate. In such instances, it will be useful to cross-refer to Part Two for more information.

It has not been possible here to deal with the situation in the European part of the Soviet Union, although some of the species concerned are included in the checklist, and due regard has been taken of them in the overall threatened species classification described in Part One. The situation in Albania is currently unclear, although the 44 species of reptiles and amphibians occurring there may be better off than in neighbouring Greece or Yugoslavia as the country is less highly developed. In addition, it appears that Albania has protected 18 species: five amphibians, all four tortoises and turtles, five lizards and four snakes (including the venomous *Vipera ammodytes*).

The order of countries generally follows a north-west to south-east sequence which broadly reflects the increasing diversity of Europe's herpetofauna (see Chapter 1). Although Iceland is a member of the CoE, it is not considered here since it does not have a native herpetofauna.

Finally, while it is recognised that certain under developed countries do need considerable help in terms of information and expertise to improve the conservation status of their herpetofauna, there is no excuse for the significant failures of countries with better resources, like the Netherlands, United Kingdom, Spain and Austria, to look after their reptiles and amphibians properly.

8
Denmark

Species Summary

Number of indigenous species: 19

Tailed amphibians:	3	*Triturus cristatus, T. alpestris, T. vulgaris*
Tailless amphibians:	11	*Bombina bombina, Pelobates fuscus, Bufo bufo, B. calamita, B. viridis, Hyla arborea, Rana temporaria, R. arvalis, R. dalmatina, R. ridibunda, R. lessonae, R.* kl. *esculenta**
Tortoises and turtles:	0	
Lizards:	3	*Lacerta agilis, L. vivipara, Anguis fragilis*
Snakes:	2	*Natrix natrix, Vipera berus*, (*Coronella austriaca* is now considered extinct)

*The 'hybrid' edible frog is treated as a species.

State of Knowledge

An unpublished file exists containing some 3,400 precisely located observations made by P. Holm Andersen in the 1940s. The most extensive mapping project so far is the 'Atlas of amphibians and reptiles in Denmark'. The survey for this was undertaken between 1976 and 1986 and the results will be published in 1989. In addition, detailed mapping of selected species has been carried out by professional biologists in a few counties during the 1980s and regular monitoring programmes have been set up for certain amphibian populations. Existing knowledge is therefore extensive and up-to-date.

Species Threats

The number of localities for *B. bombina* has greatly diminished this century and only eleven or twelve remain. Of these populations, two or three are so small that they will become extinct within in a few years unless boosted by artificial rearing. Three others are so small that there is perhaps a danger of inbreeding. Only four populations are definitely stable.

Triturus alpestris was first found in Denmark in 1949 and occupies only a small range. Its distribution has been thoroughly mapped in recent years and the total number of ponds holding *T. alpestris* is about 40, most of which are very small.

Hyla arborea was formerly widely distributed but has disappeared from 90-97 per cent of its localities since about 1945, and is now extinct in some regions. The rate of decrease is accelerating and is now between 6 and 20 per cent per year. Thus, although *Hyla arborea* is still widespread, it will soon become endangered. The causes of decline have been carefully studied. The main one seems to be eutrophication from agricultural fertilisers and household sewage. Other important factors are infilling of ponds (often illegally), ploughing of meadows and the introduction of predatory fish.

Pelobates fuscus is still widespread, but the decline since about 1945 has been 75-94 per cent. The decline is continuing unabated, and is now thought to be about 10 per cent per year. The causes of decline are similar to those for *Hyla arborea*, eutrophication being most important.

Although still widespread, the decline of *Bufo calamita* since about 1945 has been 45-77 per cent. In many regions it has disappeared from 'natural' habitats and survives only in gravel pits and other 'artificial' habitats. Protection of such habitats is usually impossible.

Still widespread in east Denmark, *Bufo viridis* has declined by 64-85 per cent since 1945 and its decline has rapidly accelerated in recent years. *B. viridis* is very sensitive to ponds becoming overgrown, but not particularly to eutrophication. Other threats are associated with the decline in traditional cattle and duck rearing and the increased intensity of such stock rearing in certain areas, and from the introduction of fish, especially in village ponds.

Rana dalmatina has not declined as seriously since 1945 (22-43 per cent reduction), but the distribution is limited and scattered and the destruction of only a few ponds could exterminate *R. dalmatina* from a whole district. Eutrophication and toxic farm chemicals seem to be the main threats.

Vipera berus is a widespread species, except in east Denmark where it is rare. *V. berus* is slowly declining as a result of loss of heathland, scrub encroachment on sunny slopes, reduced grazing and drainage of bogs.

Natrix natrix is still widespread, but has declined by 31-74 per cent since about 1945. The main threats to this species are the decline in amphibian populations, scrub encroachment of marshes and the disappearance of dung-heaps for egg-laying.

The most widespread threat to other species of amphibians is pond eutrophication. To abate this threat on a national scale would require much more money than is presently available. Therefore, there is little hope of avoiding further declines. Another major threat is changed use of ponds, particularly related to cattle and duck keeping, and the introduction of fish (mainly sticklebacks, grass carp, crucian carp and goldfish).

Conservation Measures Taken

All amphibians and reptiles have been protected in Denmark since March 1981. It is now illegal to collect or kill *Triturus alpestris*, *Bombina bombina*, *Hyla arborea* and most reptiles, in all life stages. Other amphibians may be collected as eggs or larvae. The two commonest reptiles and the five commonest amphibians may be collected in moderate numbers by schools and research institutions.

From 1978, the law on nature protection has included a provision (S.43) that no ponds greater than 1,000m², no ponds situated in an urban environment, and no marshes greater than 5ha may be destroyed or changed without permission. In 1984, S.43 was amended to cover other features such as all heathland above 1ha, and all ponds greater than 500m², and for a forthcoming revision of the law it has been suggested that all ponds greater than 250m² and all meadows above a certain size should also be protected. This very positive approach is often referred to as the "status quo" method.

The species protection law generally seems to be observed by the public. The law protecting small ponds has some effect, but it is probably often violated.

In the county of Vejle, an information pamphlet about *Hyla arborea* has been printed by the county administration and distributed to landowners by a volunteer. At Aarhus in Jutland, where *H. arborea* formerly lived, over a dozen new ponds have been created, and some 6,000 newly metamorphosed animals have been introduced from the nearest occupied locality (80 kilometres away). The objective is to restore a viable population there. The project has until now been restricted to publicly owned areas of land but an extension into privately owned land is desirable.

Of the nine remaining *Bombina bombina* localities, eight are partly or totally protected, although the protection afforded has mostly failed to counteract threats. Out of 40 ponds with *Triturus alpestris*, 20 are now in protected areas. Most other herpetofauna localities are not specially protected.

Conservation Measures Needed

Bombina bombina

For this species the following measures are required:

- Negotiations with landowners to improve site protection.
- Management or dredging of ponds.
- Extermination of introduced fish in one locality.
- Establishment of cattle grazing or attaining appropriate grazing regimes.
- Acquisition of land.

- Construction of new ponds next to existing ones.
- Artificial rearing programmes, to include exchange of genetic material between different localities.
- Monitoring of individuals, populations and habitats, including investigations into the effect of management on other organisms in the ponds.
- Implementation of a proposal for the creation of five Biogenetic Reserves for the species in Denmark.

Triturus alpestris

Half of the ponds where *T. alpestris* occurs are now officially protected, and some others are protected through private arrangements. The most urgent need is to protect the remaining ponds, purchase important areas, and provide concessions to enable farmers to continue keeping cattle where herpetofauna interests require the continuation of cattle grazing. The construction of new ponds and restoration of old ones is needed in some cases.

Hyla arborea

About half of the population is on the island of Bornholm, where the county has spent and is spending much money on restoration of eutrophicated ponds, re-laying of drainage pipes and creation of new ponds. However, there remains scope to expand these measures. Elsewhere, very little has been done for *H. arborea*. There should be more education of landowners, better administration of existing laws, restoration of many ponds and creation of many new ponds, and in at least one case, artificial rearing of a threatened population.

Other Amphibians

In several municipalities and in some regional counties, pond projects have been carried out including, for example, mapping and restoration of ponds and the eradication of introduced fish. In some cases the intention has been to help specific amphibian populations. However useful these projects have been, they are still manifestly insufficient in relation to the extent of habitat destruction and the widespread problem of eutrophication.

On a national scale, the need is more money, more projects, and more rigorous legislation and administration. There is not yet sufficient understanding of these needs amongst politicians and administrators. Educational programmes, including an information campaign to discourage fish introductions into breeding ponds, are required.

Bibliography

Fog, K. (in press). *Report on the atlas survey of amphibians and reptiles in Denmark.* Forlaget Fauna Bøger, Ganløse.

9
Norway

Species Summary

Number of indigenous species: 10

Tailed amphibians:	2	*Triturus cristatus, T. vulgaris*
Tailless amphibians:	3	*Bufo bufo, Rana temporaria, R. arvalis*
Tortoises and turtles:	0	
Lizards:	2	*Lacerta vivipara, Anguis fragilis*
Snakes:	3	*Natrix natrix, Coronella austriaca, Vipera berus*

State of Knowledge

The distribution and current status of most Norwegian reptiles and amphibians are poorly known. Data on most species, except for the newts, are quite old, and the only ecological studies to date have been on the newts, although the current status and threats to species have been considered (Dolmen 1986, 1987). It is generally known that there is a pronounced decline in the distribution of amphibian and reptile populations, and particularly of newts. Extensive investigations on the distribution, status and ecology of herpetofauna species are therefore badly needed.

Species Threats

In Norway, the following species are threatened: *Triturus cristatus, T. vulgaris, Rana arvalis* and *Coronella austriaca*. A particular threat to amphibians living in small ponds and lakes is the commercial introduction of crayfish *Astacus* in south-west Norway.

Triturus cristatus is the most threatened amphibian in Norway. The known localities in central Norway have been reduced by more than 20 per cent during the last two decades and an additional 10-15 per cent are threatened. In western Norway only a few relict local populations are left. In the south-east lowlands, however, *T. cristatus* is not uncommon in a few areas. The main reasons for its decline are draining and infilling of breeding localities or the introduction of predatory fish (especially salmonids), which quickly exterminate the larvae.

Triturus vulgaris is relatively common in some parts of central and south-east Norway, but the number of breeding localities is declining for the reasons mentioned above. However, it appears to be more tolerant of predation pressure from fish, and it is also sometimes found in larger water-bodies.

Coronella austriaca is restricted to the extreme south and south-east lowlands and coastlands where the climate is favourable. Its status here is unknown, but this area is where most people in Norway live, and many landscape changes have taken place including urban development, road construction and the building of numerous holiday homes. *C. austriaca* is often killed in mistake for *Vipera berus*.

Rana arvalis is restricted to south-east Norway with a few localities in the south. Its status is uncertain, but it is considered a rare species and the number of known breeding localities has declined over the past few years.

Conservation Measures Taken

All amphibians and reptiles have been protected by law since April 1982. Although the law also protects their eggs, nest or home, amphibian and reptile localities are steadily being disturbed and destroyed. Amphibian breeding sites are drained, filled-in, polluted or made uninhabitable in other ways, for example as a result of stocking ponds with fish. An information booklet on the need for protection of landscape elements in the countryside, including ponds and brooks, has been distributed to farmers throughout the country. No sites have yet been protected on the basis of herpetofauna conservation, but a proposal for a reserve that supports five amphibian species has recently been put forward. Norwegian national parks are usually situated in mountainous areas, while most most amphibians and reptiles are distributed in the lowlands.

In central Norway a rescue programme for newts has been initiated. Newts have been transferred to new ponds which are regarded as safe for the future and some old newt localities have been restored. The problem of introduced fish is being countered by field trials assessing the impact of Rotenone (a fish poison) on invertebrates.

Conservation Measures Needed

The first step towards conserving Norwegian amphibians and reptiles should be the initiation of a national mapping project. Such an investigation should record the habitats of the species and their dispersal routes, and analyse the limits of and possibilities for their survival. On the basis of this information it should be possible to devise and implement adequate conservation measures.

Secondly, the effects of acid precipitation, pesticides, pollution, farming and forestry practices and pollution and other negative impacts should be investigated, and possible remedial measures proposed.

Finally, on the basis of the Berne Convention, which Norway has ratified, and also the domestic legislation, the best *Triturus cristatus* localities in different parts of the country should be protected.

Bibliography

Dolmen, D. (1986) Norwegian amphibians and reptiles; current situation 1985. In: Rocek, Z. (ed.), *Studies in herpetology.* (Proc. 3rd Ord. Gen. Meet. SEH, 1985), pp. 743-746. Charles University, Prague.

Dolmen, D. (1987) Hazards to Norwegian amphibians. In: van Gelder, J. J. van, Strijbosch, H. and Bergers, P. J. M. (eds), *Proc. 4th Ord. Gen. Meet. SEH, 1987*, pp. 119-122. Faculty of Sciences (Catholica University) Nijmegen.

10
Sweden

Species Summary

Number of indigenous species: 19

Tailed amphibians:	2	*Triturus cristatus, T. vulgaris*
Tailless amphibians:	11	*Bombina bombina*+, *Pelobates fuscus, Bufo bufo, B. calamita, B. viridis, Hyla arborea, Rana temporaria, R. arvalis, R. dalmatina, R. lessonae, R.* kl. *esculenta**
Tortoises and turtles:	0	
Lizards:	3	*Lacerta agilis, L. vivipara, Anguis fragilis*
Snakes:	3	*Natrix natrix, Coronella austriaca, Vipera berus*

+Presumed extinct but re-established via re-introduction.
*The 'hybrid' edible frog is treated as a species.

State of Knowledge

The present knowledge of amphibian and reptile zoogeography in Sweden is based on work by Gislén and Kauri (1959), which is now largely out of date. Parts of the country, e.g. the west coast and the southernmost province of Skåne, are rather well known, but large parts of south-eastern, central and northern Sweden need further study. Basic information of conservation interest for all rare species is stored in a 'national data bank for endangered species', and this is regularly updated. Many rare species with restricted distributions

Sweden

have been well-studied, including *Bombina bombina*, *Rana lessonae* and *R. dalmatina*, but others having a more widespread and sparse occurrence are largely unknown, including *Triturus cristatus* and *Coronella austriaca*. Further surveys are likely to change the understanding of conservation priorities.

To obtain up-to-date information on the distribution, ecology, population status and conservation priorities of Swedish amphibians and reptiles, a national mapping project was started in 1985. Gaps in knowledge are now being checked in the field and it is hoped to publish the atlas (which contains 7,000 records) during 1990. The government is currently funding two research projects on amphibians and reptiles. Since 1981 a university research group has worked on several aspects of herpetofauna conservation problems, including the reintroduction of *Bombina bombina* in southern Sweden, the island populations of *Bufo calamita* on the west coast, the out-post populations of *Lacerta agilis* in western and central Sweden and the effects of acidification on Swedish amphibians.

One person is engaged in a university study on the *Rana lessonae* population inhabiting the Baltic coast area in northern Uppland. Another university research group has focused on the habitat requirements and genetic variation in the *Rana dalmatina* populations in Skåne and on Öland.

Species Threats

As in other west European countries traditional small-scale farming and forestry have changed into large-scale cropping during the last 50 years or so. Most species of amphibians and reptiles have declined in numbers and range, but the consequences in detail for survival are not well known. Parts of Sweden also suffer from airborne pollution, especially acid precipitation, which particularly affects amphibian reproduction. A particularly serious situation has recently arisen for amphibians, namely the commercial introduction of alien species of crayfish to thousands of ponds and lakes in southern Sweden. The best site for *H. arborea* in northern Europe is now considered at risk.

Two species, *Bombina bombina* and *B. viridis* are seriously threatened. *B. bombina* had continuously decreased for more than 100 years in

Sweden, finally becoming extinct in 1960. It was reintroduced at four sites in Skåne between 1983 and 1985, and these sites now sustain small breeding populations. *B. bombina* mainly occurred in uncultivated and undrained marshy areas and pasture, habitats which are rare on modern farms.

B. viridis is one of Sweden's most endangered vertebrates, occurring in only about ten small coastal populations in Skåne, Blekinge and on the Baltic island of Öland. The reasons for the small population size and local decrease or loss are mainly unknown. The number of adults at each of the remaining ten sites varies from five to about 50 at the best breeding sites. The populations of three species, *Bufo calamita, Lacerta agilis* and *Coronella austriaca* are much depleted and are regionally threatened.

There are two separate areas of distribution of *B. calamita* in Sweden, one on small rocky islands in the outer west coast archipelago and the other in sandy inland and coastal areas in the south. The west coast populations are not endangered, but many small and isolated populations are morphologically distinct. Most of the southern sandy soil populations have decreased or become extinct during recent decades. Habitat destruction due to agricultural and industrial development or road construction and forestry is the principal cause of the decline.

In northern areas, populations of *L. agilis* are a relict from the postglacial warm period of 9,000 to 2,500 years ago when the species was probably widely distributed in southern and central Sweden. The range today is more scattered with a more or less continuous, though retreating, range in the south-eastern and southernmost parts, with some very small populations along the west coast and in central Sweden. *L. agilis* occurs in two different types of habitat, the most common being moving sand dunes of partly overgrown sand pits, but also exposed rocky or slaty slopes. Declines continue with local extinctions in Skåne, the most recent example being the loss of the Ven Island population. The most serious threats to the northern populations are loss of open sand by scrub encroachment and loss of genetic variation in very small and isolated populations.

The Nordic populations of *C. austriaca* are restricted to the west coast of Sweden, extending to southern Norway, and to the east coast extending to Uppland province. The Nordic population of *C. austriaca* has probably been isolated for about 8,000 years and has ecologically distinctive features, living mainly in rocky habitats and feeding on other reptiles such as *Vipera berus*. *C. austriaca* is rarely observed because of its secretive choice of habitat under rocks or in the upper soil layer and its status and population dynamics are largely unknown. The threats to this rarely seen species are therefore difficult to define.

More information is needed to define and counteract the degree of local threat suffered by *Triturus cristatus, Hyla arborea, Pelobates fuscus, Rana dalmatina* and *Rana lessonae*.

T. cristatus has a widespread but sparse distribution across Sweden except the northernmost parts, and it is often sympatric with the more common *T. vulgaris*. The status and population dynamics of *T. cristatus* in Sweden are not well known, and there is an urgent need for more information on its biology, habitat requirements and population size. Its reproductive behaviour is currently being investigated.

H. arborea is dependent on a specific habitat structure with grasses, bushes and trees surrounding breeding ponds. In 1982 a total of 3,500 calling males were counted in 236 localities in central and eastern Skåne. About 20 per cent of the population was recently lost due to the construction of an airport in central Skåne. *H. arborea* is not immediately threatened, but habitat destruction could easily change the situation, especially through the planting of conifers.

The distribution of *P. fuscus* is confined to areas of sandy soil in south and south-west Skåne, including intensively used agricultural areas. Information about its biology, population size and status is limited because of its mainly nocturnal activity. The main threats to *P. fuscus* are loss or deterioration of small water bodies, and road mortality during movements in spring to breeding ponds and in summer when large numbers of metamorphosed toads leave the ponds. Its status is insufficiently known, but it is probably not yet seriously threatened.

The Swedish population of *R. lessonae* is restricted to less than 60 small local populations along the northern coast of Uppland province. All the breeding ponds are situated in a narrow ephemeral zone where shallow coastal waters provide suitable habitat for breeding after being cut off from the sea but before being invaded by scrub and forest. The nearest continental populations are found about 1,000km to the south. The Swedish population of *R. lessonae* seems to be morphologically and genetically distinct from these. The species is not immediately threatened, but forestry and drainage are the main reasons for extinctions of local populations.

Three different populations of *R. dalmatina* are found in south-east Sweden: one in eastern Skåne, one in Blekinge and one on Öland. The Swedish (and Danish) populations are geographically well separated from the continuous continental populations, and preliminary investigations suggest (Ahlén 1984) that they are genetically distinct. *R. dalmatina* is dependent on deciduous forest with a specific structure giving the best climatological conditions for premetamorphic development. The species is not seriously threatened, but loss of habitat, by, for example, felling of woodlands or planting of conifers, could quickly change the situation.

Finally, there is the specific problem faced by the isolated population of *Natrix natrix gotlandica* on the Baltic island of Gotland. This snake is morphologically and ecologically distinct, with smaller size and different scalation and pattern compared to mainland populations. The extensive loss of smaller water-bodies on Gotland during the recent decades poses a serious threat not only to the survival of this population, but also to the morphologically distinct population of *Rana arvalis* on the island. A few smaller populations of *N. n. gotlandica* are found on rock islets off the main island and, remarkably, they live mainly in the Baltic Sea where they feed on marine fish.

Conservation Measures Taken

Since 1985 ten of the Swedish amphibians and reptiles have been legally protected and can only be removed from their natural populations for scientific purposes. Some rare species are protected in nature reserves or by restrictions on land use. Many endangered species are still decreasing in numbers mainly because of habitat destruction, but sometimes for unknown reasons. For other sparsely distributed species, the nature of threats to the population is not well known. In 1987 a new law came into force giving the local district authorities more responsibility for nature conservation matters. However, very few local administrations have competent biologists on their staff. To date, at the local level, economic interests have had priority over protection of important amphibian sites.

A careful study of the distribution of *B. viridis* by the University of Göteborg, has been combined with a captive breeding programme to strengthen small populations and increase their genetic variability. The re-introduction of *B. bombina* from Danish stock into a series of 20 ponds is continuously monitored and seems to have been successful. Conservation management is now being applied to safeguard the northern outposts of *L. agilis*.

Conservation Measures Needed

Professor Ingemar Ahlén has suggested that conservation measures for rare amphibians in Sweden should not be confined to protecting a few of the best populations by the creation of large nature reserves, but focus on the many small important habitats such as breeding ponds and their immediate surroundings. Additionally, it has been suggested that specific land use restrictions should be applied to the entire distributional range of threatened species. In this way many more local populations could be saved and conditions improved to ensure the long term survival of threatened species. This approach may be particularly worthwhile for *Hyla arborea, Rana dalmatina, R. lessonae, Pelobates fuscus, Bombina bombina* and perhaps *Lacerta agilis*.

Species listed in Appendix II of the Berne Convention should be given not only nominal protection, but their habitats should be properly protected. Nature conservation authorities, especially at the local level, have not fully understood their obligations towards the Berne Convention in this respect. Despite an increased awareness and interest in reptiles and amphibians in recent years, conservation still holds a weak position in the face of development threats and other economic pressures.

The serious problem posed by commercial crayfish farming must be addressed urgently, and negotiations are now underway between conservationists and the agriculture authorities.

Bibliography

Ahlén, I. (1986) Skyddet av hotade arter. *Sveriges Natur* 77, 12-15.

Andrén, C. and Nilson, G. (1981) Distribution and conservation of endangered Swedish reptile and amphibians. *Proc. Eur. Herp. Symp. Oxford 1980,* 65-67.

Andrén, C., Nilson, G., Sjögren, P. and Larsson, T. B. (1988) Nature conservation research on amphibians and reptiles in Sweden. In Espic, L. E., Hansson. L., Larsson, T. B., Moberg, A. and Svensson, L. (eds). *Protection of nature and natural resources.* Stockholm. 12 pp. SNV Report (in press).

Gislén, T. and Kauri, H. (1959) Zoogeography of the Swedish amphibians and reptiles. *Acta Vertebr.* 1, 197-397.

11
Finland

Species Summary

Number of indigenous species: 10

Tailed amphibians:	2	*Triturus cristatus, T. vulgaris*
Tailless amphibians:	3	*Bufo bufo, Rana temporaria, R. arvalis*
Tortoises and turtles:	0	
Lizards:	2	*Lacerta vivipara, Anguis fragilis*
Snakes:	3	*Natrix natrix, Coronella austriaca, Vipera berus*

State of Knowledge

The provisional atlas of the Finnish amphibian and reptile species is based on information received through comprehensive enquiries, records in the literature and specimens in the collections of the zoological museums in Finland up to 1980. An estimated population status for each species is also provided. Some material dating from the 1980s has been received, but additional recent data on the status, sites and habitats of threatened species are needed.

Species Threats

Triturus cristatus has a disjunct distribution with populations in south-east Finland (representing outposts of Russian populations) and the Aland archipelago in south-west Finland where it evidently originates from Sweden. Local populations are small and in danger

145

of extermination from human activities such as more intensive land use, construction and road traffic.

C. austriaca has only been recorded on the main island of the Aland archipelago. The population is sparse, but there is no precise information on habitats and sites. Increasing tourism and traffic, changes in agricultural practices and a negative attitude to snakes by the general public seem to be its most important threats.

Conservation Measures Taken

According to the Finnish government's statute No. 404/83, all native amphibian and reptile species with the exception of *Vipera berus* are protected. However, individuals and tadpoles of *Rana* spp. *Bufo bufo* and *Triturus vulgaris* can be collected for educational or scientific purposes. These provisions are also included in Resolution 41/77 for the autonomous Province of Aland in south-west Finland. Legislation protects species of no economic importance for man, unless otherwise stated.

Conservation Measures Needed

Finnish amphibian and reptile species represent marginal elements of the more diverse central and south European herpetofauna. Monitoring the distributions and population status of species in the northernmost areas of their ranges should be continued in cooperation with parallel ecological research projects in other countries.

The habitats and current status of the two threatened species, *T. cristatus* and *C. austriaca*, should be assessed by means of intensive field work. On the basis of this information, negotiations with land owners should be commenced in order to protect the most important sites. Public awareness relating to the identification and ecology of the two species, should be improved through increased coverage in the media.

Bibliography

Terhivuo, J. (1981) Provisional atlas and population status of the Finnish amphibian and reptile species with reference to their changes in northern Europe. *Ann. Zool. Fennici* 18: 139-164.

12
Poland

Species Summary

Number of indigenous species: 27

Tailed amphibians:	5	*Salamandra salamandra, Triturus cristatus, T. alpestris, T. montandoni, T. vulgaris*
Tailless amphibians:	13	*Bombina variegata, B. bombina, Pelobates fuscus, Bufo bufo, B. calamita, B. viridis, Hyla arborea, Rana temporaria, R. arvalis, R. dalmatina, R.* kl. *esculenta*, R. lessonae, R. ridibunda*
Tortoises and turtles:	1	*Emys orbicularis.*
Lizards:	4	*Lacerta viridis, L. agilis, L. vivipara, Anguis fragilis*
Snakes:	4	*Elaphe longissima, Natrix natrix, Coronella austriaca, Vipera berus*

*The 'hybrid' edible frog is treated as a species.

State of Knowledge

Survey and mapping efforts have been very variable with some local regions well covered, but most of the country has not been comprehensively assessed. Two of the rarest species, *Emys orbicularis* and *Elaphe longissima*, now have such restricted ranges that their distribution is known in detail. Many sites have been mapped for

Bufo calamita and *Pelobates fuscus* and the montane distribution of *Bombina variegata* is thought to be well recorded.

A comprehensive account of the status of the Polish fauna and its conservation needs was published in 1980. This concluded that the reptiles and amphibians were the most seriously threatened animal groups but that considerably more field data were required before an accurate and detailed assessment of the problems could be made.

Species Threats

Amphibian populations are generally declining due to a combination of factors adversely affecting their breeding waters, including infilling of ponds, pollution and land drainage. The export of green frogs has been a considerable problem but may now be controlled under recent legislation. Although habitat destruction is the main reason for the decline of reptiles and amphibians in Poland, national experts also consider that pollution, especially from pesticides, and deliberate killing and collection are equally serious causes of decline.

In the 1960s, the few remaining populations of *Lacerta viridis* were dependant on a combination of dwarf shrub vegetation and a sandy substrate. Since this time it is not clear how many (if any) populations survive or whether any of their sites have been protected. *Rana dalmatina* is now very localised, considered endangered, and dependant on small sunny ponds which are themselves very vulnerable. *Emys orbicularis* and *Elaphe longissima* are also considered endangered, but no data on their precise status are available. *Coronella austriaca* is known to be rare and declining, although its secretive nature suggests that more detailed field surveys may be required to ascertain its precise status and conservation needs.

Conservation Measures Taken

Three reserves have been declared for *Emys orbicularis* ranging from 4.5 to 300 hectares in extent. Two reserves of 20 and 50 hectares, have been declared for *Elaphe longissima*. Sensibly, some of these have been achieved by simply extending the boundaries of national parks to encompass core habitats for these endangered species.

Nearly all reptiles and amphibians are strictly protected. It is illegal to catch, injure, kill, keep, trade or translocate them without a licence issued for sound scientific reasons. While this measure is laudable, two of the most endangered and persecuted species, *Lacerta viridis* and *Vipera berus* are not protected, and neither are the green and brown frogs. Attempts are still underway to amend the law so that these species are partially or totally protected.

Conservation Measures Needed

The anomalies in protective legislation need to be rectified, especially for *Rana dalmatina, Lacerta viridis* and *Vipera berus*. Habitat protection must also be achieved for the first two species. *Emys orbicularis* and *Elaphe longissima* need recovery plans and more protection through designation of nature reserves. A recovery plan for *Lacerta viridis* should also be designed and urgently implemented.

Protective habitat legislation is needed for ponds and small lakes, and this should take account of the potential negative impact on *Triturus* species of stocking such waters with fish.

13
Czechoslovakia

Species Summary

Number of indigenous species: 31

Tailed amphibians:	6	*Salamandra salamandra; Triturus cristatus, T. dobrogicus, T. alpestris, T. vulgaris, T. montandoni*
Tailless amphibians:	13	*Bombina bombina, Pelobates fuscus, Bufo bufo, B. calamita, B. variegata, B. viridis, Hyla arborea, Rana temporaria, R. arvalis, R. dalmatina, R.* kl. *esculenta*, R. lessonae, R. ridibunda*
Tortoises and turtles:	1	*Emys orbicularis*
Lizards:	6	*Lacerta viridis, L. agilis, L. vivipara, Podarcis muralis, Anguis fragilis, Ablepharus kitaibelii*
Snakes:	5	*Elaphe longissima, Natrix natrix, N. tessellata, Coronella austriaca, Vipera berus*

*The 'hybrid' edible frog is treated as a species.

State of Knowledge

The broad distribution of most reptiles and amphibians is known at national level and there have been a number of regional surveys which have produced data at a site level. However, significant gaps in knowledge exist for some of the rarer species: *Triturus montan-*

doni, **Pelobates fuscus, Rana arvalis, R. dalmatina, Bufo calamita, Emys orbicularis** and **Ablepharus kitaibelii**. A recent survey to confirm the possible occurrence of *Podarcis taurica* in the south-east failed to locate this species. During 1989 a similar survey was being undertaken in the south-west for the possible occurrence of *Vipera (ursinii) rakosiensis.*

Species Threats

The most threatened species are considered to be *Triturus cristatus, T. dobrogicus, T. montandoni, Bufo calamita, Hyla arborea, Emys orbicularis, Podarcis muralis, Ablepharus kitaibelii, Elaphe longissima* and *Natrix tessellata. Pelobates fuscus* is also said to be rare but this might be a function of its elusive habitats. Concern must also be expressed for *Vipera berus* in its lowland and sub-montane habitats where it has become increasingly rare in recent years.

With the exception of the forest-living species *Salamandra salamandra* and *Triturus alpestris,* most amphibians are now declining due to agrochemical usage, enrichment of fish ponds, drainage of small streams, swamps and marshes, collection for vivaria and collection for laboratory use. The main threats to reptiles are habitat destruction, collection for vivaria and deliberate killing (especially of snakes). A typical example of the latter problem was recorded in 1988 at the *Natrix tessellata* reserve where its use for recreation resulted in more than 100 snakes being killed.

Conservation Measures Taken

Seventeen species are protected in Bohemia and Slovakia. *Hyla arborea* and *Ablepharus kitaibelii* are also protected in Slovakia where there is a scale of penalties ranging from 4,500 Crowns for these species down to 200 Crowns for all species of the genus *Bufo.* However, there is no evidence that these penalties have been applied. Several nationally rare species remain unprotected although amendments to existing conservation legislation to cover all reptiles and amphibians have been proposed since 1982.

A few areas have been specially declared for herpetofauna. Two Protected Faunal Sanctuaries have been designated in Slovakia for *Lacerta viridis, Podarcis muralis* and *Ablepharus kitaibelii*, each several hundred hectares in extent. A river gorge locality for *Natrix tessellata* and *Lacerta viridis* has been protected, and the southern exposures of Bratislava Castle are now managed to maintain the Castle's colony of *Podarcis muralis*.

The first project to reduce road mortality of *Bufo bufo* has recently been started and has received wide publicity in the district of Beroun.

Conservation Measures Needed

Field surveys should be undertaken to identify the most important sites for those threatened species for which there are information gaps: *Triturus montandoni, Rana arvalis, R. dalmatina, Bufo calamita* and *Emys orbicularis*.

Rationalisation and better implementation of protective legislation is overdue and more species should be protected, including *Hyla arborea* in Bohemia and *Rana arvalis, R. dalmatina* and *Vipera berus* throughout the country. The most threatened species should be accorded appropriate habitat protection as a matter of urgency.

Special, albeit small, reserves should be declared for *Triturus montandoni* and for groups of south Bohemian ponds supporting breeding populations of *T. dobrogicus, Pelobates fuscus, Bufo calamita, Hyla arborea* and *Rana arvalis*.

A public education programme against snake persecution is needed, especially to prevent the killing of *Natrix tessellata*.

14
Democratic Republic of Germany

Species Summary

Number of indigenous species: 27

Tailed amphibians:	5	*Salamandra salamandra, Triturus vulgaris, T. alpestris, T. helveticus, T. cristatus*
Tailless amphibians:	14	*Alytes obstetricans, Bombina variegata, Bombina bombina, Pelobates fuscus, Bufo bufo, B. calamita, B. viridis, Hyla arborea, Rana arvalis, R. dalmatina, R. temporaria, R. kl. esculenta*, R. lessonae, R. ridibunda*
Tortoises and turtles:	1	*Emys orbicularis*
Lizards:	4	*Anguis fragilis, Lacerta agilis, L. viridis, L. vivipara*
Snakes:	3	*Coronella austriaca, Natrix natrix, Vipera berus*

*The 'hybrid' edible frog is treated as a species.

State of Knowledge

Information on distribution and status of amphibians in most of the 15 districts of the GDR is reasonable but there is less information on the reptiles. A nationwide mapping programme at a scale of 1:25,000 is currently being coordinated. Recent results have been published for Thuringia, Saxonia, and the districts of Halle, Magdeburg, Frankfurt/Oder, and are in preparation for the districts of Neubrandenburg, Schwerin and Rostock. A national synthesis will be published in the next few years. This will be primarily based on field data from the past 10-15 years. For the following species ecological studies have been carried out and the details published: *Lacerta viridis, L. agilis, Vipera berus, Pelobates fuscus, Bufo calamita, B. viridis* and European frogs.

Field studies (data unpublished) have also been carried out for *Bombina variegata, Rana dalmatina* and *Salamandra salamandra*.

Species Threats

Three species are considered endangered: *Bombina variegata, Emys orbicularis,* and *Lacerta viridis.* The north-eastern boundary of the range of *Bombina variegata* passes through the south-western hill and mountain region of the GDR, with the centre of distribution in the district of Erfurt. Further populations occur in Gera and Suhl districts. Factors contributing to the endangered status of *B. variegata* are the stocking of waters with fish, infilling of breeding sites, pollution and general habitat destruction. Illegal collection for the pet trade was also significant in the past.

The distribution of *Emys orbicularis* is centred in the north (Mecklenburg/Brandenburg) with isolated localities in the districts of Leipzig, Dresden and Magdeburg. Causes of decline include climatic factors, but are mainly drainage, pollution and fragmentation of populations.

Only two populations of *Lacerta viridis* now remain, in the Frankfurt/Oder and Cottbus districts. Climatic restrictions, habitat change and isolation of populations are thought to be the primary reason for the endangered status of this species.

Nine species are considered vulnerable: *Salamandra salamandra, Triturus cristatus, T. helveticus, Bombina bombina, Hyla arborea, Lacerta agilis, Natrix natrix, Coronella austriaca* and *Vipera berus.*

Salamandra salamandra is present in the southern mountains region and the Harz Mountains. It is threatened by pollution, intensive cattle farming and destruction of breeding waters.
Triturus cristatus is present throughout the country but there are

many gaps in distributional data. It is threatened by drainage, pollution and infilling of ponds and stocking of ponds with fish.

The range of *Triturus helveticus* is confined to the south-west of the country and the Harz Mountains (eastern border of distributional range) where it is endangered by drainage of pools, fish stocking and the destruction of small ditches on forest roads.

The western border of the European distribution of *Bombina bombina* runs through the GDR with a population centre in the Mecklenburg districts. This species has declined through the drainage of ponds, pollution of waters by agricultural chemicals and household detergents, stocking fish, intensive cattle rearing and infilling of breeding sites.

Hyla arborea is found in the northern part of the country (Mecklenburg districts) with scattered localities in the central GDR and some southern districts. *H. arborea* has declined due to the loss of breeding sites, pesticides use, fish stocking and destruction of summer basking and feeding sites (e.g. hedges). The pet trade has contributed to its decline, particularly around Berlin.

Lacerta agilis occurs throughout the GDR with some gaps in distribution in the districts of Halle and Erfurt. It is threatened by afforestation of uncultivated areas, infilling of quarries and pits, pesticides and population isolation (in the north).

Natrix natrix is present throughout the GDR, with its centre of distribution in Mecklenburg and Brandenburg. *N. natrix* has declined through pollution, loss of open water sites and loss of amphibian prey items.

Coronella austriaca is mainly distributed in the districts of Gera, Leipzig and Dresden with scattered localities in the north. Habitat destruction, afforestation and the decline of prey items *(Lacerta* spp.) are the main factors causing decline of *C. austriaca.*

The main populations of *V. berus* occur in the southern mountainous region of the GDR and along the Baltic Sea coast. Habitat destruction due to intensive agriculture and forestry have been the main reasons for decline.

Two species are considered rare: *Alytes obstetricans* and *Rana dalmatina*. The eastern border of the European distribution of *Alytes obstetricans* is in the south-west GDR (Thuringia and Harz Mountains). *A. obstetricans* has declined as a result of destruction of breeding sites, pollution of ponds, poultry farming and stocking of waters with fish. Scattered populations of *Rana dalmatina* are present in Saxony, the Harz Mountains, the Darss Peninsula and Rügen Island. The populations are of reasonable size and some of the habitats are declared as protected areas, such as in the Planitzwald in Leipzig district. However, acidification of waters is becoming a problem, including in the Planitzwald nature reserve.

Conservation Measures Taken

All amphibians and reptiles have been protected by law ('Artenschutzbestimmung') since October 1984. Some of the big nature reserves are very important for herpetofauna. For example 'Papitzer Lehmlachen' (Leipzig district), 'Ostufer der Müritz' (Neubrandenburg district) and 'Hinrichshagen' (Neubrandenburg). Most herpetological orientated reserves are between three to five hectares and there are many of them in the GDR. In some districts there are around 100. Additionally, some military training areas are important for reptiles and amphibians.

Aerial spraying of pesticides provides many problems, especially for amphibian breeding waters, and the protection of some of the smaller reserves is very difficult. Habitat management is practised mostly by honorary workers sometimes in connection with agricultural cooperatives. In the middle and southern parts of the country many breeding ponds of amphibians and reptile habitats are managed. Captive breeding projects are under way for *Lacerta viridis* and are in preparation for *Emys orbicularis*.

Conservation Measures Needed

Registration and protection of reptile habitats must take place and be enforced. A top priority, in international terms, is to protect species which are widespread or have their European centres of distribution in the GDR and which are generally threatened in Europe. Important and large breeding site complexes of such species must be protected as should semi-natural habitat types which are important for these species (e.g. damp meadows for *Rana arvalis* and *Rana temporaria*). Some of the most important areas should be protected as Biogenetic Reserves. Another international priority is to maintain populations of those species which are at the edge of their European range in the GDR, including *Triturus helveticus*, *Bombina variegata* and *Alytes obstetricans*. Similarly, conservation measures must be enacted to maintain those species which have only relict populations in the GDR, such as *Rana dalmatina*, *Emys orbicularis* and *Lacerta viridis*.

A staff of two or three professional herpetologists who specialise in the native herpetofauna should be established and herpetofauna conservation problems must be given a higher profile in public relations and education. Special attention is required for *Lacerta viridis*, *Emys orbicularis* and *Bombina variegata*; measures required include intensive field studies for the latter two species. Field studies of all species should be undertaken, especially for reptiles and to investigate small isolated reptile populations and their dynamics. The size and status of isolated populations should be investigated and documented.

A further priority is to formulate a plan for protecting and managing mineral excavations and xerothermic habitats. These habitats are greatly threatened: mineral excavations are commonly used for waste disposal and xerothermic habitats, particularly those in intensive agricultural landscapes, need to be protected from pollution by agrochemicals and other aspects of intensive agriculture.

Efforts have to be improved to map amphibian breeding sites during the next few years throughout the whole of the GDR. Important breeding sites should not only be declared as protected areas but damaging agricultural activities should be prohibited in them and around them. A management programme is needed to protect temporary and small pools in agricultural areas from drainage.

Bibliography

Günther, R. and Schiemenz, H. (in prep.) *Die amphibien und reptilien der DDR*. Gustav Fischer Verlag, Jena.
Nöllert, A. and Nöllert, Ch. (1987) Herpetofaunistische und allgemeine

herpetologische Forschung für das Gebiet der DDR von 1949-1984 (Amphibia et Reptilia). *Zoolog. Abh. Staatl. Mus. Tierkd.* Dresden Bd. 43/Nr. 6, 49-99.

15

Federal Republic of Germany

Species Summary

Number of indigenous species: 32

Tailed amphibians:	6	*Salamandra salamandra, S. atra, Triturus alpestris, T. helveticus, T. vulgaris, T. cristatus*
Tailless amphibians:	14	*Alytes obstetricans, Bombina bombina, B. variegata, Pelobates fuscus, Bufo bufo, B. calamita, B. viridis, Hyla arborea, Rana arvalis, R. dalmatina, R. temporaria, R.* kl. *esculenta*, R. lessonae, R. ridibunda*
Tortoises and turtles:	1	*Emys orbicularis*
Lizards:	5	*Anguis fragilis, Lacerta agilis, L. viridis, L. vivipara, Podarcis muralis*
Snakes:	6	*Coronella austriaca, Elaphe longissima, Natrix natrix, N. tessellata, Vipera berus, V. aspis*

*The 'hybrid' edible frog is treated as a species.

State of Knowledge

A Red List for the Federal Republic of Germany has been compiled and nearly all of the 11 federal states have their own Red List. However, the level of information on amphibians and reptiles in the FRG varies greatly. Surveys are in progress in each of the eleven federal states but only a few have been completed, some only at county level. Data on amphibians (mapping of breeding sites) are much more complete than data for reptiles. Results of recent surveys have been published for most of the federal   states (Schleswig-Holstein, Hamburg, Lower Saxony, Bremen, Northrhine-Westphalia, Rhineland-Palatinate and Baden-Württemberg). Because of the different levels and methodologies of survey a nation-wide synthesis is not currently planned.

The distribution and status of some species (e.g. *Bombina bombina, Lacerta viridis, Elaphe longissima, Natrix tessellata, Vipera aspis*) have been well documented as a result of special surveys, and ecological investigations (e.g. habitat requirements) are underway for many other species in different regions.

Species Threats

Seventy-five per cent of the reptiles and 55 per cent of the amphibians are considered threatened. Many species have experienced serious decline over the last 40 years. These declines follow intensification of agriculture (including official land exchange to consolidate farms) and other activities which have degraded or destroyed habitats for the species such as intensive forestry, urbanisation, peat digging, stocking of water bodies with fish, pollution by agrochemicals and acidification of surface waters due to acid rain. Riverine species such as *Natrix tessellata* have been affected by leisure activities and river engineering works.

The most endangered species are considered to be *Bombina bombina, Emys orbicularis, Lacerta viridis, Elaphe longissima, Natrix tessellata* and *Vipera aspis*. Six other species are rare or localised and must be considered as threatened: *Bufo viridis, Hyla arborea, Rana arvalis, Rana dalmatina, Podarcis muralis* and *Vipera berus*. Another eight species are known to be declining and are vulnerable: *Alytes obstetricans, Bombina variegata, Bufo calamita, Pelobates fuscus, Rana ridibunda, Triturus cristatus, Coronella austriaca* and *Natrix natrix*.

Bombina bombina is considered as endangered in the FRG, and it occurs only in the north-east (Schleswig-Holstein and Lower Saxony). The species has become extinct in the Aller valley within the last few decades. The causes of its dramatic decline (60 per cent of sites have been lost from Lower Saxony since 1915) and the subsequent isolation of populations may be partly related to climatic changes, but habitat destruction has been the major factor. Of most significance have been drainage, cultivation of pasture, pollution, infilling of ponds, river regulation and fisheries management.

Bufo viridis is also considered endangered in the FRG and the north-western limit of its range passes from the south-west to the north-east of the country. There has been a dramatic decline in some areas. For instance, only 9 sites for the species now remain in Lower Saxony whereas there were 26 sites in 1975. The reasons for its decline are the same as for *B. bombina* - most notably, habitat destruction and stocking of waters with fish.

Apart from the higher mountains, *Hyla arborea* is distributed throughout the FRG. It has suffered a serious decline over the last 40 years, particularly in the uplands, and has declined by 50 per cent in Lower Saxony.

Although generally occurring in the lowlands, *Rana arvalis* is found throughout the FRG except in the high mountains. It is more threatened in the south of the country and has declined by up to 30 per cent in Lower Saxony.

The current northernmost limit of the range of *Rana dalmatina* passes south of the River Elbe. In the north there are only a few relatively isolated populations, while population density is higher in the south. The present isolation of much of the population in the FRG is probably related to removal of deciduous forest, a process which began many centuries ago. More recently intensive forestry, water abstraction, infilling of breeding sites, pollution, fish stocking and road traffic have further reduced populations of this species.

Though individuals of *Emys orbicularis* have been reported from several localities in the north of the FRG, *E. orbicularis* is considered to be extinct, at least as a breeding species. Recent observations are probably related to attempts to reintroduce the species or escapes from captivity. Long-term changes in climate, collecting and use for human consumption during Lent in historic times, persecution by fishermen and habitat degradation have all contributed to the extinction of *E. orbicularis*.

There are known to be several isolated, mostly small, populations of *Lacerta viridis* in Bavaria, Baden-Württemburg and Rhineland-Palatinate. The main area of distribution is around the 'Kaiserstuhl' and central Rhine region. A succession of cool, wet summers in the 1980s may have lowered the hatching and survival rate of eggs and young. Intensive viticulture, land consolidation, pesticides, afforestation, scrub encroachment on xerophytic meadows and long-term changes in climate have all contributed to the decline of *L. viridis*.

Podarcis muralis is at the edge of its European range in the FRG where it occurs in localised areas within the main regions of viticulture such as in the river valleys of the Rhine, Ahr, Mosel, Lahn and Neckar. It has been successfully introduced in several places such as at Passau. The decline of *P. muralis* in the FRG has been the result of land consolidation and agricultural intensification in areas of viticulture (removal of stone walls, levelling of slopes, use of biocides, use of large machinery). The cultivation of waste land, road construction, development of sunny slopes, infilling of old quarries, repairing of old walls and scrub encroachment have been additional factors which have removed suitable habitat. Isolated populations at the edge of the range are vulnerable to the unfavourable weather.

There are several relict populations of *Elaphe longissima*, most of them fragmented, occurring in Bavaria, Baden-Württemberg and with the northernmost populations in Hessen (especially 'Rheingau'). Knowledge about its distribution is good owing to the recent completion of special mapping projects. It has declined due to habitat destruction but has also been subject to persecution and collection. The removal of dung heaps has been an additional negative factor since these are occasionally used for egg laying.

Only three isolated relict populations remain of *Natrix tessellata* remain, all in Rhineland-Palatinate (valleys of the rivers Mosel, Lahn and Nahe). These are the northernmost sites in western and central Europe and are well separated from the main European area of distribution. There has been a dramatic decline of more than 80 per cent. It is extinct in the Rhine Valley, and the remaining population is estimated to be between 100 and 150 individuals, with an unbalanced age structure. The main causes of decline have been water engineering works and intensive river management, restoration of old walls, recreation, pollution and possibly climatic factors. *Vipera berus* no longer occurs in southern Northrhine-Westphalia, western Hessen, Rhineland-Palatinate, Saarland and parts of Baden-Württemberg, especially the warmer regions where vines are cultivated along the rivers Rhine, Main, Neckar and numerous tributaries. However, it is still quite widespread in the northern lowlands of the FRG. A decline of 90-95 per cent has been reported for *V. berus*, but this may be too high although there has undoubtedly been a catastrophic decline in some regions. Habitat destruction has been the main reason for this decline.

Vipera aspis occurs in only one small area on the southern edge of the Black Forest, which represents the most north-eastern locality of its European range. It is one of the rarest reptiles with a population numbering a maximum of 200 adults, rediscovered in 1979, having been previously considered as extinct. The decline of *V. aspis* has been mainly caused by intensive forestry and agriculture, killing and collecting. Recent climatic changes, namely lower mean average temperatures, reduced sunshine hours and successive cool, wet summers may also have affected it.

Conservation Measures Taken

Since 1980, when the Federal Regulation Concerning the Conservation of Species (Federal Nature Conservation Act 1976) came into force, all 32 native amphibians and reptiles have been protected. Collecting, killing, trading and keeping, as well as the destruction of their habitats is prohibited. Legal protection does not, however, cover agriculture, forestry and fisheries. This means that the existing regulations are far from satisfactory, despite the fact that legal protection for special biotopes was improved by an amendment of the Federal Nature Conservation Act in 1987, to comply with the Berne Convention. Nature conservation has had little effect in the FRG, especially with respect to habitat protection. The principal reason for this is that responsibility for nature conservation lies with the federal states (länder). Because of the poor enforcement of conservation legislation and the inadequate protection of habitats, numerous sites of herpetological importance are threatened.

Some small areas, particularly small ponds and flooded pits, have been protected and are managed for their herpetological importance. Species which have benefited include *Bombina bombina, B. variegata, Alytes obstetricans, Bufo viridis, Hyla arborea* and *Natrix tessellata*. In other nature reserves or monuments, many species have benefited as a result of protection afforded by such designations, although management of these areas may not be adequate or particularly suitable to the special requirements of those amphibians and reptiles which are present. Some military training areas provide excellent habitats for amphibians and reptiles. In addition, numerous private nature conservation bodies are active in managing existing sites and creating new ones for amphibians and reptiles.

Conservation Measures Needed

It is vital to prevent further extinctions and habitat loss. However, it will be difficult to arrest declines without better knowledge of the status and distribution of species and their specific ecological requirements. Therefore, a survey and mapping of the whole country should be undertaken to investigate the habitats, ecological requirements and distributions of threatened species and habitats which are suitable for them. Such surveys should be repeated on a regular basis.

Meanwhile, comprehensive protection should be afforded to all known populations of endangered species and to key habitats for all threatened ones. The Federal Nature Conservation Act and the good knowledge of breeding ponds offers the possibility of making systematic plans for amphibian conservation, and notably for establishing amphibian reserves in each federal state. The first objective should be to define a network of the most important breeding ponds covering the whole range of species. In selecting sites, criteria should be: species richness, occurrence of rare or threatened species and population size. One of the highest priorities in this regard should be the protection and declaration of the proposed Biogenetic Reserve 'Fevestorfar Elbwiesen' as a key area for *Bombina bombina*.

An attempt should be made to reunite isolated neighbouring populations of threatened species by creating suitable habitats between important sites. Such measures could be promoted through the creation of nature reserves or monuments but could also be implemented through plans for forestry and other land use (agricultural extensification and set-aside for example).

In many cases the establishment of protected areas alone will not adequately conserve the herpetofauna of the FRG. Specific long-term management plans for the conservation and development of biotopes throughout the countryside (e.g. heathland, xerophytic meadows) should be produced, where tourism and intensive agriculture are prohibited. Traditional land use would be permitted, providing this was compatible with the nature conservation objectives. Special attention also needs to be paid to breeding ponds. Degraded ponds require restoration and new pools need to be created to compensate for lost ones. Such actions could help to re-establish species in areas where they have become extinct in recent times, for example for *Hyla arborea*.

For some species, feasibility studies on captive breeding and reintroduction should be undertaken. For example, *Natrix tessellata* has an unbalanced population structure which could benefit from a programme of captive breeding and reintroduction.

Collaboration over research, survey and the application of conservation measures mentioned above will be important and will necessitate close cooperation between nature conservation authorities, institutes and universities.

Bibliography

Blab, J., Nowak, E., Trautman, W. and Sukopp, H. (eds) (1984) *Rote Liste der gefährdeten Tiere und Pflanzen in der Bundesrepublik Deutschland*. 4. Aufl. - Greven (Kilda), 270 pp.

Blab, J. (1986) *Biologie, Ökologie und Schutz von Amphibien*. 3. Aufl. - Greven (Kilda), 150 pp.

16
Netherlands

Species Summary

Number of indigenous species: 23

Tailed amphibians:	5	*Salamandra salamandra, Triturus cristatus, T. alpestris, T. vulgaris, T. helveticus*
Tailless amphibians:	11	*Bombina variegata, Alytes obstetricans, Pelobates fuscus, Bufo bufo, B. calamita, Hyla arborea, Rana temporaria, R. arvalis, R. ridibunda, R. lessonae, R.* kl. *esculenta**
Tortoises and turtles:	0	
Lizards:	4	*Lacerta agilis, L. vivipara, Podarcis muralis, Anguis fragilis*
Snakes:	3	*Natrix natrix, Coronella austriaca, Vipera berus*

*The 'hybrid' edible frog is treated as a species.

State of Knowledge

The distribution of amphibians and reptiles in the Netherlands is well known and all distribution data up to 1983 have been published. Several mapping projects are underway, collecting new and recent data. The data are stored in national and provincial data banks. However, in spite of great efforts, some species lack sufficient distribution data for conservation purposes, for example *Anguis fragilis* and *Pelobates fuscus*. For some species, the information needs to be updated, including that for *Rana arvalis, Lacerta agilis* and *Coronella austriaca.* The situations of the rarest species (*Podarcis muralis, Bombina variegata, Hyla arborea* and *Alytes obstetricans*) are well known.

Species Threats

At present the most endangered species are *Bombina variegata, Hyla arborea* and *Podarcis muralis.* Six more have become rare or of localised occurrence and must be considered as threatened. These are *Salamandra salamandra, Triturus cristatus, Alytes obstetricans, Rana arvalis, Lacerta agilis* and *Coronella austriaca.* A further five species are known to be declining: *Triturus alpestris, Triturus helveticus, Lacerta vivipara, Natrix natrix* and *Vipera berus.* More information is needed to determine the true status of *Pelobates fuscus, Anguis fragilis* and *Rana arvalis.* More details about these species are given in the following section.

The Netherlands is a densely populated country and most remaining natural and semi-natural habitats are very small, poorly protected or subject to damaging external impacts such as pollution and acidification. In addition, small, yet important, features such as hedges, walls, ponds and copses are all being lost. Habitat loss, alteration and fragmentation remain the major threats to Dutch amphibians and reptiles, and are caused by agricultural intensification, commercial forestry (including afforestation), urban and industrial development, military use, tourism and recreation. Commercial collecting badly affects the rarest species. Other damaging activities include inappropriate grazing regimes, burning, peat cutting and clearance of watercourses.

Conservation Measures Taken

Since 1973, all native reptile and amphibian species have been fully protected under the Nature Conservation Act (NCA), which forbids their capture, killing, keeping and sale (attempts included). It is also forbidden to disturb the animals, including their 'nests'. *Emys orbicularis* is covered by the NCA, although it is not indigenous to the country. Excluded from protection are the eggs, larvae and young of frogs (genus *Rana*), and it is possible to obtain exemptions from these provisions. The habitats of all species are also theoretically protected under the Berne Convention, which was ratified in 1979 and brought into force in 1982.

There is no effective conservation policy for herpetofauna in the Netherlands. A few sites have been designated under the NCA as a 'Protected Nature Monuments', which assures the survival of the site, but does not guarantee appropriate management. Some other areas have been designated as 'nature areas', for instance in urban development plans, as a form of protection against town and country planning developments. In general, however, the habitats of protected species may be destroyed, damaged, fragmented or polluted due to modern agricultural practices, forestry, road construction or housing development and no protective action can be taken. Their interests are given a low priority and official bodies do not stand up for them. Even the last site of the rarest species, *Podarcis muralis,* threatened with extinction, is not yet protected, in spite of demands from nature conservationists for over ten years.

A positive development is that of 'pool programmes'. At a provincial level, programmes are formulated, funded and executed for the construction of pools and ponds favourable for amphibians, particularly for rare species, such as *Hyla arborea, Bombina variegata, Alytes obstetricans* and *Triturus cristatus.*

Conservation Measures Needed

In general, habitats need to be safeguarded, restored, and recreated, and adequate site management programmes implemented. For the endangered and rare species the current situation and detailed requirements are given below.

Bombina variegata is only found at three localities in the south of Limburg. Two sites have tiny populations and their chances of survival are uncertain, although they are situated inside nature reserves. Pollution and stocking of the sites with fish needs to be prevented. The site holding the only viable population (an aging population of approximately 100 individuals) is a marl pit that was declared a 'Protected Nature Monument' in 1987. Reproduction there has been at an extremely low level for years. Most of the shallow pools in the pit dry up too early. The creation and appropriate management of new pools with a guaranteed water level is the priority requirement. Additionally, use of the site for clay-pigeon shooting should cease and controls on the use of the site for geological investigations are required. Stricter control on access is required in order to deter collection of *B. variegata*, as has also happened recently.

Hyla arborea occurs in four isolated areas, and is declining in all of them except for a single locality in the province of Limburg. Its aquatic habitats, most of which are situated in agricultural areas, are being filled in and polluted. The main populations in each of the different areas should be protected as 'Nature Monuments'. The creation of new pools to compensate for lost ones, management of aquatic vegetation and conservation of terrestrial scrub and tall herb vegetation are additional measures required to conserve and enhance populations of *H. arborea*. In the province of North-Brabant, a breeding programme might prevent regional extinction. Collection of *H. arborea* must be prevented.

The Netherlands population of *Podarcis muralis* is the most northern in Europe, and therefore is of particular biological importance. Protection of the last remaining site is extremely urgent, since only some tens of individuals are left, and they do not reproduce every year. The site, situated in the middle of the city of Maastricht, should be given the status of 'Protected Nature Monument' immediately and closed to the public and their dogs. The restoration of the old walls ought to stop, or be modified to allow the retention of crevice systems between and behind the bricks. In addition, vegetation in the dry moats and on the tops of the walls should be kept short, perhaps by heavy sheep grazing. The appointment of a warden might be useful for site control, to eliminate feral cats from the area and to increase public awareness about *P. muralis*. A breeding programme for lizard eggs that have been deposited too late for successful hatching might help supplement the population.

Salamandra salamandra is restricted to the south of Limburg, and to some localities in Gelderland and Overijssel which support very few individuals. In Limburg, the main population lives in a deciduous forest with wells and brook systems. The lower parts of the brooks are cleaned too frequently for questionable 'water-level management', and parts of them serve as drainage ditches for a railway that crosses the forest and they are polluted by herbicides.

There is currently a serious threat due to reconstruction of the railway embankment in which the major part of the population is found. Some other isolated brooks also harbour *S. salamandra* and these are very vulnerable to the effects of agriculture. Monitoring of these populations is necessary and further information needs to be collected regarding the situation in Gelderland and Overijssel.

Triturus cristatus has suffered the greatest decline of all newts in recent years. Causes include the infilling, pollution and drying up of pools, loss of terrestrial habitats and probably the introduction of predatory fish. The creation of new pools at suitable places, and appropriate management of them might lead to a recovery, but the priority is clearly to conserve the stronger surviving populations and their breeding ponds.

Alytes obstetricans has a similar range to *Bombina variegata* and is restricted to south Limburg. The locality of the largest population, a sand and gravel pit, was designated as a 'Protected Nature Monument' in 1986, just in time to prevent it becoming a refuse dump. However, the site is not entirely safe due to its use by motorcyclists and the continuing problem of vegetation succession. Another protected marl pit holds both *B. variegata* and *A. obstetricans* and its pool system must also be kept intact.

Rana arvalis has experienced a significant decline in the Netherlands, but there is little information about its current status. Although it favours acid moorland and heathland pools for breeding, such pools are vulnerable to acidification. It is important that localities for *R. arvalis* outside nature reserves should be safeguarded and that buffer zones around these sites are also safeguarded to protect vulnerable pools from adverse external influences.

Lacerta agilis has also experienced a serious decline during recent decades, but no population figures are available. Its habitat (dry heathland, with mature heather stands) has suffered greatly from afforestation, fires and trampling. The quality of heathland habitats in the Netherlands has deteriorated in recent years owing to a combination of dry summers and cold winters, encroachment of grass (due to nutrient enrichment) and heather beetle plagues. Moreover, old heather (over 15 years) is not yet recognised as the optimum habitat for many heathland species, including other reptiles, so management practices have tended towards encouraging younger heather stands to the probable detriment to *L. agilis*. Mowing, grazing and burning of heathlands are practised but are not ideal for conserving heathland reptiles. Turf-cutting is the best method for regenerating heathland, but for reptiles it should be practised only occasionally and on a small scale, especially since the inappropriate use of the 'Plaagen machine' (a mechanical turf-stripper) has recently caused widespread damage to some heathland sites. Modification of current heathland management techniques, fire prevention and the provision of open sandy areas for egg-laying are essential for the survival of *L. agilis*. Sand lizards also live in coastal sand dunes where their decline is probably associated with vegetation succession causing shading and loss of open sandy areas.

Coronella austriaca is the Netherlands' second rarest reptile. It is secretive and lives at low densities so little is known about its specific habitat requirements. However, in heathlands, its needs are much the same as for *L. agilis*, except that it does not need open bare sand. In forests, clearings must be available. More survey is required.

17
Belgium

Species Summary

Number of indigenous species: 24

Tailed amphibians:	5	*Salamandra salamandra, Triturus alpestris, T. cristatus, T. helveticus. T. vulgaris*
Tailless amphibians:	12	*Alytes obstetricans, Bombina variegata, Pelobates fuscus, Hyla arborea, Bufo bufo, B. calamita. Rana arvalis, R. dalmatina, R.* kl. *esculenta*, R. lessonae, R. ridibunda, R. temporaria*
Tortoises and turtles:	0	
Lizards:	4	*Anguis fragilis, Lacerta agilis, L. vivipara, Podarcis muralis*
Snakes:	3	*Coronella austriaca, Natrix natrix, Vipera berus*

*The 'hybrid' edible frog is treated as a species.

State of Knowledge

The overall distribution of Belgian amphibians and reptiles is quite well known. All distributional data up to 1984 have been collected and published. No mapping projects are underway, but a number of individuals are involved in collecting further distributional data. However, information about many species is still insufficient for conservation purposes.

Existing Conservation Measures

In Belgium, a distinction has to be made between the Flanders region and the Wallonia region, because they have different circumstances concerning the protection of fauna. In Flanders, by an Order in Council of 1980, all amphibians and reptiles are legally protected, with the exception of *Rana temporaria* and the green frog complex. The order prohibits hunting, catching, keeping, killing or transporting them, damage and disturbance to their habitats. It is also forbidden to catch or kill *R. temporaria* and green frogs, except for private nursery ponds. Exemptions from these provisions can be granted for reasons of scientific, educational or general interest. In Wallonia, a regional act of 1983 protects all native amphibians and reptiles, with the exception of *R. temporaria* and green frogs, and the responsible Minister for Nature Conservation has to agree exemptions from the act's provisions. Belgium signed the Berne Convention in 1979, but has not yet ratified it. However, this ratification is expected soon, which means that in the near future the habitats of all species should receive due protection.

Belgium lacks an effective conservation policy for amphibians and reptiles. Local authorities have few options for taking positive conservation action as responsibilities lie at the regional level (Flanders, Wallonia, Brussels), but the regions are currently failing to pursue any positive measures for reptile and amphibian conservation.

Species Threats

There is no official Belgian 'Red List' for reptiles and amphibians, but their status over the past 100 years and threats have been described Parent (1984). Using these data and incorporating the views of other Belgian herpetologists, the following list of threatened species has been produced: *Alytes obstetricans, Bombina variegata, Bufo calamita, Hyla arborea, Pelobates fuscus, Rana arvalis, Rana dalmatina, Salamandra salamandra terrestris, Triturus cristatus, Triturus helveticus, Anguis fragilis, Lacerta agilis, Podarcis muralis, Coronella austriaca, Natrix natrix helvetica, Vipera berus.*

More details about these species are given in the following section. Most of their habitats are not adequately protected by buffer zones to ameliorate external influences. Loss of habitat, drainage, pollution and collection are the main threats, but fires, recreational disturbance and fish farming are also significant.

Conservation Measures Needed

Bombina variegata was once found across the east and south of the country, but after severe declines it may now only be present in the province of Liège. *B. variegata* has declined as a result of infilling of cattle drinking pools, drainage, water pollution, use of old quarries for storage purposes, stocking of ponds with fish, afforestation of forest glades and marshes, upgrading and even asphalting of forest rides, and collection. It needs absolute protection of all its remaining habitats, more appropriate forestry management, control of collection and monitoring of the situation. This is most urgent, not least because the situation for this species in northwestern Europe as a whole is deteriorating.

Pelobates fuscus is insufficiently known, but it is a very rare species found in Flanders, the Campine and at Bergen/Mons. Its few localities need strict protection and a survey of its distribution and status is required.

Hyla arborea has a widespread but now fragmented distribution over the whole of Belgium, with key concentrations in West Flanders and in Limburg. The heavy decline of *H. arborea* has been caused by infilling, drainage and pollution of pools and marshes, intensification of land use and road construction. Locally, it may have been affected by introduction of fish. One important site is now threatened by excavation in connection with the construction of an international water-skiing centre. Sites which still support it must be safeguarded, together with adequate buffer zones around them.

Rana dalmatina is now extremely rare and is known from only one locality in the south-east, close to the Luxembourg border. Total protection of the known sites is urgently needed.

Salamandra salamandra lives in the south, south-west and east of Belgium. It is threatened principally by the loss of springs, wells and brooks through canalisation, camping pressure, and conversion of natural forests into plantations with upgraded rides. *S. salamandra* has also been subject to intense pressure from collecting. Forests with wells should be strictly conserved, with special protection afforded to those few populations which bear albinos, neotenous specimens, or the red morph 'var. *coccinea*'.

Triturus cristatus is widespread in Belgium, but has declined significantly due to the destruction of large pools, lowering of water-tables, urbanisation, water pollution, collection by children and pet dealers, and introduction of predatory fish such as sun perch (*Lepomis gibbosus*) and rainbow trout (*Salmo gairdneri*). *T. cristatus* must be protected by the creation of nature reserves, and by strict control against commercial collection.

Alytes obstetricans is found in the south and east of Belgium and has suffered primarily from habitat destruction, pollution and the stocking of fish in pools used for egg-laying. The creation of protected areas is urgently needed to halt the decline.

Bufo calamita is found over much of Belgium. The causes of its decline include destruction of breeding areas, lowering of water-tables, use of pesticides, afforestation of open habitats such as heathlands and marshes, use of quarries for storage or motorised sports and destruction of terrestrial habitats for tourist accommodation. All of the surviving sites for *B. calamita* should be safeguarded and properly managed, plus new sites created.

Rana arvalis is restricted to the Campine (provinces of Antwerp and Limburg). It has become rare because of marshland drainage and lowering of the water-table. Nature reserves must be created in order to prevent its extinction.

Lacerta agilis is restricted to Belgian Lorraine, where it is very rare. Habitat destruction of heathlands and species rich grassland by fires, afforestation, road construction, and town development has been the primary cause of decline. Apart from the poor condition of heather stands, the surviving habitats are isolated and too small. The introduction of pheasants has been locally damaging, as has the gassing of holes and burrows of foxes and rabbits, where *L. agilis* may hibernate. This harmful practice should be banned in areas occupied by *L. agilis*.

Podarcis muralis is restricted to the basin of the River Meuse, where approximately 100 scattered populations occur. Improved country-side access has meant the construction of roads and paths along slopes with suitable habitats, and a lack of vegetation management has resulted in the shading of habitats. Measures are required to minimise these impacts, while old walls in populated areas require protection. More applied ecological research on *P. muralis* is needed.

Coronella austriaca occurs mainly in south-east Belgium, but its distribution extends north-west to the provinces of Antwerp, Limburg, Brabant and Hainault. The decline of *C. austriaca* has been caused by deterioration of heathlands through fires and other impacts, and the disappearance of hedges. Many of the snakes are killed, often in mistake for *Vipera berus*. Any further fragmentation of heathland and species rich meadow should be prevented. Additionally, edge habitats, hedges, quarries and ruins should be protected. A public awareness programme is needed to discourage people from killing snakes, especially this harmless and rare species.

Natrix natrix has a similar distribution to *C. austriaca*, but is absent from Antwerp and Limburg. *N. natrix* occupies large home ranges and is therefore very sensitive to habitat barriers, particularly roads. Its riverine habitats have been disturbed by the construction of bar-rages. In common with other snakes it is often killed. It is very difficult to protect all the habitats of this species, but its needs should be considered in development plans, especially with regard to egg-laying sites.

Vipera berus occurs in the provinces of Namur and, rarely, Antwerp. Its habitats are being reduced and destroyed by heathland afforestation. Pheasants may be a significant predator. Improved conservation awareness of the public is desperately needed to discourage the extensive and uncontrolled killing of *V. berus*. Secrecy about the location of its remaining sites might help to protect it.

Bibliography

Parent, G. H. (1984). Atlas des Batraciens et Reptiles de Belgique. *Cahiers d'Éthologie Appliquée, Liège*, 4(3): 1-198.

Sparrenboom, M. (ed.) (1981) *De amfibieën en reptielen van Nederland, België en Luxemburg.* A. A. Balkema, Rotterdam.

18
Luxembourg

Species Summary

Number of indigenous species: 20-22

Tailed amphibians:	5	*Salamandra salamandra, Triturus alpestris, T. cristatus, T. helveticus, T. vulgaris*
Tailless amphibians:	9-10	*Alytes obstetricans, Bombina variegata, Hyla arborea, Bufo bufo, B. calamita, Rana dalmatina, R.* kl. *esculenta*, R. lessonae, R. ridibunda⁺, R. temporaria*
Tortoises and Turtles:	0	
Lizards:	4	*Anguis fragilis, Lacerta agilis, L. vivipara, Podarcis muralis*
Snakes:	2-3	*Coronella austriaca, Natrix natrix, Coluber viridiflavus#*

*The 'hybrid' edible frog is treated as a species.
+The occurrence in Luxembourg of *R. ridibunda* has not been confirmed.
#*C. viridiflavus* has not been recorded since 1950 and is presumed extinct.

State of Knowledge

The overall distribution of reptiles and amphibians in Luxembourg is well known. Distributional data have been collected and published. A mapping project is underway by a Study Group of the

Musée d'Histoire Naturelle de l'État, but the information is not yet sufficiently detailed for conservation purposes.

Species Threats

A Red Data List has been published and the comparative status and threats to species assessed. Using these data, the following list of threatened species has been derived (it includes all but two of the country's indigenous species): *Salamandra salamandra, Triturus cristatus, T. alpestris, T. vulgaris, T. helveticus, Bombina variegata, Alytes obstetricans, Bufo bufo, Bufo calamita, Hyla arborea, Rana temporaria, R. dalmatina, R. esculenta, Lacerta agilis, Lacerta vivipara, Podarcis muralis, Anguis fragilis, Coluber viridiflavus, Natrix natrix helvetica, Coronella austriaca*. All species suffer from habitat destruction, including drainage and pollution.

Conservation Measures Taken

Except for *Rana temporaria* and *R. esculenta*, all species are fully protected under the Act for the Conservation of Nature and Natural Resources of 1982, and by a National Order of 1984. This means that it is forbidden to catch, kill or disturb animals, and to trade them. The National Order of 1984 has a special regulation concerning green frogs and brown frogs such that their capture is permitted within private grounds. Luxembourg has ratified the Berne Convention.

The 'Fondation Hellif fir de Natur', subsidised by the Luxembourg State Government, is buying as many important habitats as possible for the protection of herpetofauna. Some new ponds are also being created.

Conservation Measures Needed

Alytes obstetricans has been badly affected by infilling of its spawning waters. Road mortality is high and road tunnels are needed to alleviate this problem.

Bombina variegata has declined due to drainage, canalisation and underground culverting of watercourses. Habitat creation and protection for *B. variegata* are urgently needed.

Bufo calamita has declined as a result of loss of breeding habitats through drainage, excavation, infilling and premature drying up of suitable ponds. Remaining *B. calamita* sites should be protected and new ones created.

While *Rana dalmatina* may already be extinct in Luxembourg, its last known site should be protected and carefully monitored.

Salamandra salamandra is threatened by pollution of streams and replacement of deciduous forests by conifer plantations. It is relatively well protected in the remaining deciduous forests, but the planting of conifers needs to be discouraged or restricted. In some places, tunnels under roads are needed on migration routes.

Triturus cristatus is often locally abundant, but it is rare on a national level and threatened by infilling and pollution of ponds. Creation of new ponds in suitable areas might alleviate the decline of *T. cristatus*.

The preferred habitats of *Lacerta agilis* include forest edge and low scrub in sunny situations. Many such habitats are being destroyed. *L. agilis* is additionally vulnerable to cat predation. Protection of habitats and proper management of them are needed.

Podarcis muralis inhabits dry, rocky areas, such as vineyards, as well as walls. It is threatened by renovation of walls (e.g. re-pointing), and by pesticides used to spray the vine crops. Cat predation is a further threat.

Coronella austriaca is threatened by habitat loss and indiscriminate killing by people.

Natrix natrix is normally associated with standing or running water. It is threatened by excavation, water pollution, and from persecution by humans. A decrease in the natural food supply, e.g. fish and amphibians, may have played some part in its decline.

Coluber viridiflavus was recorded in the 1950s but is now almost certainly extinct.

Bibliography

Parent, G.H. (1984). Atlas des Batraciens et Reptiles de Belgique. *Cahiers d'Éthologie Appliquée, Liège*, 4(3): 1-198.

Sparreboom, M. (ed.) (1981) *De amfibieën en reptielen van Nederland, België en Luxemburg*. A.A. Balkema, Rotterdam.

19
United Kingdom

(i) GREAT BRITAIN

Species Summary

Number of indigenous species: 12-14

Tailed amphibians:	3	*Triturus cristatus, T. vulgaris, T. helveticus*
Tailless amphibians:	3	*Rana temporaria, Bufo bufo, B. calamita,* *(Hyla arborea*)*
Tortoises and turtles:	0	
Lizards:	3	*Lacerta agilis, L. vivipara, Anguis fragilis,* *(Podarcis muralis*)*
Snakes:	3	*Natrix natrix, Coronella austriaca, Vipera berus*

*One population of each of these species might possibly be native.

State of Knowledge

Data on the distribution and status is known at site level and regularly updated for *Bufo calamita* and *Lacerta agilis*. Distributional data and information on the status of *Coronella austriaca* are also available. Additionally, data are currently being accumulated on amphibians, with special regard for *Triturus cristatus*. For the eight remaining more common species, general distribution patterns have been recorded on a 10km tetrad, mainly using literature sources rather than recent field investigations. Changing trends in the local status of amphibians and reptiles have been deduced from the results of a questionnaire survey. The habitat requirements of *Bufo calamita, L. agilis and Coronella austriaca* have been studied and are well understood.

Species Threats

Lacerta agilis is the most endangered member of the British herpetofauna. It is nearly extinct from its sole surviving sand dune range in north-west England, while the bulk of its estimated population of 5,000 adults is confined to lowland heaths in the Weald and in southeast Dorset. It has declined due to loss of heathland, compounded by the further vulnerability of sites brought about by fragmentation; continual encroachment of exotic pines from commercial plantations; encroachment of birch (*Betula* species) and bracken (*Pteridium aquilinum*), particularly after fires; fires; agriculture; erosion from public and military uses; collectors; and predation by cats..

Coronella austriaca is naturally a fairly rare animal. It has an estimated adult population of about 3,000, confined entirely to heathland in southern England. The reasons for its decline are broadly the same as for *Lacerta agilis*, although because of its longer life span and large home range it has proved more able to survive the immediate adverse effects of fire.

Bufo calamita is thought to have an adult population of around 20,000 individuals, mostly spread around the coastal sand dunes of East Anglia and north-west England and the marshes of the Solway Firth in Scotland. Less than 100 adults are all that remain in its formerly extensive heathland range. The decline of its heathland populations has been due to habitat destruction resulting from agriculture and forestry, and to the loss of open conditions in those areas that remain.

Additionally, the species requires waters with a relatively high pH for successful breeding, and these are relatively rare on the generally acid heaths. Acidification of pools due to conifer afforestation and from 'acid rain' would appear to be further contributory factors. Moreover, *B. calamita* suffers adverse competition from *Bufo bufo* populations on some sites due to an increase in tree cover. The latter factor is becoming an increasing threat at sand dune localities, although the major threats here remain recreational pressure and expansion of holiday resorts.

Although relatively widespread, *Triturus cristatus* is the rarest and most rapidly declining of the remaining five amphibians. It is a poor coloniser and generally associated with areas which historically held natural pools, and where there is adequate terrestrial habitat within close reach of the breeding site. A proposal to safeguard, as Sites of Special Scientific Interest (SSSIs), an arbitrary 100 of the best populations from its estimated 6,500 breeding sites is not considered adequate not least because site loss is more rapid than the time required to survey and decide which sites should be designated.

Natrix natrix appears to be declining throughout its cooler north European range, including the UK where its egg-laying sites have shifted from natural habitats (such as rotting vegetation left by river floods) to manure heaps, saw-dust piles and compost heaps in gardens. Such substitute breeding habitats are less common today, and gardens are hardly safe for either the adult snake or its eggs.

In lowland England, *Vipera berus* relies on open habitats (particularly heathland, chalk and limestone grasslands) which are being lost to afforestation, agriculture, urbanisation and scrub encroachment. The status of *V. berus* in moorland in the British uplands is poorly known, though the effects of regular moorland burns may be detrimental. Persecution is a further problem: signs such as "Beware Adders" are not infrequent, often employed to deter trespass but which simply serve to perpetuate the myth that adders should be exterminated.

Conservation Measures Taken

In response to Berne Convention requirements, strict protection against disturbance, killing or taking is afforded to the four endangered and vulnerable species. However, under the Wildlife and Countryside Act (1981), protection against disturbance or killing by habitat destruction is not applicable if 'any otherwise lawful activity which could not reasonably have avoided the incidental damage to animal and habitat' is undertaken. There are many such legal activities, so loss and damage to 'protected' species and their habitats continues as a result of this loophole, especially since planning permission granted for urban developments override the provisions of the Wildlife and Countryside Act.

The eight 'commoner' species have been afforded almost no protection. Although their commercial sale is subject to a licence system no limits are set in terms of numbers that can be caught and sold, and no data on site sources or extent of collection are required, only on numbers sold. This system therefore does not control exploitation "to prevent local impoverishment" as required by the Berne Convention. An amendment in 1988 to Schedule 5 of the Wildlife and Countryside Act banned the deliberate killing of three of the reptiles, but as it excluded *Vipera berus* the main problem of killing 'look-alike' snakes remains and needlessly puts at risk *N. natrix, A. fragilis* and even the protected *C. austriaca*. Following the listing of *Triturus cristatus* as a protected species, local efforts are being made by the Nature Conservancy Council to safeguard some breeding ponds (for example, against development threats), where data on these are available.

Many of the important localities for *Bufo calamita, Lacerta agilis* and *Coronella austriaca* are designated as SSSIs. This designation seeks to control activities likely to damage the special interest of the designated sites, including agricultural and forestry operations. However, despite this, many SSSIs continue to be damaged or deteriorate, largely as a result of urban developments, fires, or because traditional management practices such as grazing and scrub cutting are no longer practised.

Several National Nature Reserves (1 in Galloway, 2 in Merseyside, 2 in Norfolk and 5 in Dorset) are important for *B. calamita, L. agilis* and *C. austriaca*. Of these, Holton Heath, Studland and Godlingston are particularly important for reptiles.

Some important sites are privately managed by voluntary nature conservation bodies, though locally perceived priorities may override the needs of nationally rare species. Comparatively large areas of undeveloped land are under the control of the Ministry of Defence and in many of these areas their wildlife conservation groups have played an important part in promoting the conservation of rare herpetofauna. The Forestry Commission has recently agreed to the designation and management of small protected sites for

L. agilis and *C. austriaca* within its southern conifer plantations.

Conservation Measures Needed

The UK government does not adequately fulfill all its obligations under the Berne Convention, particularly with respect to protecting the habitats of threatened species listed by the Convention. Two of the actions required to amend this situation are that the 'incidental damage' loophole in the Wildlife and Countryside Act must be removed or amended, and that sites designated as SSSIs must be assured of better protection and appropriate positive management. Both will require amendments to be made to the Wildlife and Countryside Act.

Other amendments are required to the species protection provisions of the Wildlife and Countryside Act, including a prohibition on the killing of all snakes, including *Vipera berus*. With respect to the continuing persecution of snakes, a public education campaign should be initiated to comply with the unfulfilled conditions of the 1978 Council of Europe (Council of Ministers) Resolution No. 22 (see Appendix II). Secondly, the aberrant licence system which allows the unrestricted exploitation of eight of the twelve native species by the pet trade should be replaced by much stricter and enforceable controls or perhaps, as in our neighbouring countries, by a complete ban. These amendments are the minimum necessary if Britain is to fully comply with her obligations to protect amphibians and reptiles as laid down by the Berne Convention.

More National Nature Reserves are clearly needed: relevant sites have been identified and proposed, but unfortunately the overall UK programme of NNR acquisition has been halted in response to present government antipathy regarding state ownership of land and their proposal to sell NNRs to private bodies.

The principal conservation need for both *Lacerta agilis* and *Coronella austriaca* is to ensure the future of the small number of lowland dry heaths that they inhabit. The overall spread of pine, birch and bracken and the lack of fire-break precautions on heathlands all require a large and continual resource input. The Wildlife and Countryside Act has provisions to promote management agreements for SSSIs whereby the costs of site work are not borne by the owner, but there is as yet no means of enforcing such essential management against an owner's wishes. It appears that some owners of privately-owned heathland have a positive wish to see their heathlands deteriorate and diminish in wildlife value, making the probability of urban development or forestry more likely on such sites. The Wildlife and Countryside Act should be amended to make positive management enforceable and hence made comparable to legislation for the maintenance of architectural heritage. Without such a provision, many important lowland heathlands will continue to be inadequately managed, will be increasingly susceptible to severe fires and land speculation, and will continue to decline in wildlife value.

Populations of *Lacerta agilis* in north-west Britain (a morphologically and ecologically distinct geographical race within the Berne Convention definitions), require legal intervention to prevent damage caused by unlimited car use of the sand dune foreshore over a critical stretch of the SSSI.

Following the successful re-introductions of *L. agilis* in the Weald, similar attempts should be made in the New Forest (Hampshire) from which it has recently become extinct through unsuitable habitat management. Serious consideration should also be given to introducing *L. agilis* to protected sand dune sites within the natural range of the species, in order to offset previous extinctions from dune systems.

Immediate priority should be given to restoring the ailing heathland population of *Bufo calamita* in Norfolk, and projects to re-introduce *B. calamita* to localities within its former range in Surrey, Suffolk, the New Forest and Dorset should be continued.

The decline of *Triturus cristatus* over much of its continental range should be seen as added justification for safeguarding a healthy UK population and range while there is still an opportunity to do so. This would require the active conservation of many more sites than is presently envisaged. Tree Preservation Orders (TPOs) are a legal mechanism used to impose planning and felling constraints on trees and woodland. A system of 'PPO's (Pond Preservation Orders) would be one logical way of reducing the widespread infilling and pollution of small ponds, so protecting *T. cristatus* and other amphibians. Adoption of the Danish licence system under their *status quo* legislation would be another way to ensure prior investigation before a site was needlessly lost. Other conservation problems facing ponds include neglect and desiccation, the latter due to lowering of water-tables following land drainage or water abstraction. Field surveys of all surviving ponds must be accelerated, and resources found for managing and protecting the most important ones. Some further respite could be gained if current proposals to protect amphibian communities as SSSIs were to be implemented.

Field research is required to determine the apparent plight of *Natrix natrix*. Its breeding sites must be located, protected, and where necessary, maintained. A field investigation into the status of *Vipera berus* is needed in order to identify its conservation requirements.

Detailed distribution and status data, particularly regarding egg-laying sites, are urgently required for *Natrix natrix* and *Vipera berus*. The situation of the *H. arborea* and *P. muralis* colonies in the New Forest and the Isle of Wight cliffs should be investigated. Both species are in Appendix II of the Berne Convention and the natural habitat of *P. muralis* seems to merit conservation attention.

Bibliography

Nature Conservancy Council (1983) *The conservation of endangered amphibians and reptiles*. Nature Conservancy Council, Peterborough.

(ii) CHANNEL ISLANDS

Species Summary

Number of indigenous species: 7

Tailed amphibians:	1	*Triturus vulgaris*
Tailless amphibians:	2	*Bufo bufo, Rana dalmatina*
Tortoises and Turtles:	0	
Lizards:	3	*Lacerta viridis, Podarcis muralis, Anguis fragilis*
Snakes:	1	*Natrix natrix*

State of Knowledge

The island of Jersey supports all the seven species of amphibians and reptiles indigenous to the Channel islands, of which the four most endangered, *Lacerta viridis, Podarcis muralis, Natrix natrix* and *Rana dalmatina* do not occur naturally on the other islands although there is a small and ailing (introduced) population of *Lacerta viridis* on Guernsey. The distribution and status of *L. viridis* and *P. muralis* have recently been determined and are reasonably well known for *Rana dalmatina*. The situation of *N. natrix,* however, is poorly known, and requires urgent investigation.

Species Threats

Rana dalmatina is near extinction: one of the two remaining sites seems likely to be adversely affected by reservoir construction and the other is being shaded by planted willow (*Salix* sp.) and is subject to water abstraction during the tadpole growth period. Other sites have been lost to drainage, pollution and vegetation succession.

The populations of *Podarcis muralis* on Jersey appear small but stable. They are confined to the close proximity of old walls, so restoration of old brickwork is a serious threat to their survival, especially when carried out during the hibernation period.

Once distributed throughout Jersey, the stronghold of *Lacerta viridis* is now sand dunes and maritime cliffs of the south-west. Elsewhere it has become restricted to a few isolated and vulnerable localities. The causes of its decline are not fully understood but are strongly suspected to be due to agricultural intensification, urbanisation and cat predation. The colour of the Jersey populations of *L. viridis* suggests that it may be a variety distinct from that in neighbouring Brittany.

It is hard to account for the rarity of *Natrix natrix* on Jersey, though a degree of past persecution may have contributed to its rarity. The Jersey population is characterised by a general lack of the distinctive collar.

Conservation Measures Taken

In Jersey, legal protection for amphibians and reptiles comprises a ban on their sale and a recently introduced provision that allows the designation of sites in a manner similar to the SSSI system of Great Britain. However, very few sites have been proposed for protection and even then most of these have been for their botanical value rather than importance for fauna. Although the Channel Islands lie within the responsibility of the UK government with respect to the Berne Convention, ratification on their behalf was not made until 1988, and then with inexcusable reservations on all species other than birds. Yet *R. dalmatina*, *L. viridis* and *P. muralis* are all listed in Appendix II of the Berne Convention, meriting strict protection and nowhere could their conservation be more pressing in the UK than on Jersey.

Conservation Measures Needed

Legislation should be enacted immediately to protect all species listed in Appendix II of the Berne Convention and their habitats. The reservations entered by the Channel Islands over Berne should be withdrawn.

The habitats of *Rana dalmatina* should be subject to a prompt programme of protection, restoration, enhancement and, where necessary, re-creation of breeding pools. Sites should also be monitored regularly during the breeding season.

All important *Lacerta viridis* localities should be protected and, where necessary, managed to maintain their mosaic of deep grasses, herbs and low shrubs, as well as suitable substrates for egg-laying.

Proper provision should be made for the needs of *Podarcis muralis* before any management of their walls and the surrounding grounds is undertaken. Tree and scrub shade of *P. muralis* sites must be minimised.

Field research should be initiated to determine the status and habitat needs of *Natrix natrix*, followed by subsequent site protection and habitat management where appropriate.

United Kingdom

(iii) NORTHERN IRELAND

Species Summary

Number of indigenous species: 4

Tailed amphibians:	1	*Triturus vulgaris*
Tailless amphibians:	2	*Rana temporaria, Bufo calamita*
Tortoises and turtles:	0	
Lizards:	1	*Lacerta vivipara*
Snakes:	0	

State of Knowledge

The general distribution patterns of the amphibians and reptiles have been recorded on a 10km tetrad within the overall UK atlas, but only using literature sources rather than field investigations.

Conservation Measures Taken and Needed

Northern Ireland has a separate system of conservation legislation, and is not covered by the Wildlife and Countryside Act. However, the Areas of Scientific Interest (ASIs) that can be declared by the Northern Ireland Department of the Environment are analogous to the SSSIs of Great Britain.

The UK's ratification of the Berne Convention on behalf of Northern Ireland has been so couched in "reservations" that the faunal implications have been minimal. Similarly there are few nature reserves and only slow progress to notify protected Areas of Scientific Interest. However, the passing of a Wildlife Order in 1985 has given strict protection (on paper) to *Triturus vulgaris* and *Lacerta vivipara*. The Order also contains provisions for habitat protection, but it is doubted that any such positive moves have yet been implemented. In any case, in the absence of detailed distributional and site data for these two species, their systematic conservation cannot be promoted.

Field surveys should be promoted for *Triturus vulgaris* to assess reported pond losses, and for *Lacerta vivipara* in order to protect significant populations.

20
Eire

Species Summary

Number of indigenous species: 4-5

Tailed amphibians:	1	*Triturus vulgaris*
Tailless amphibians:	2	*Rana temporaria, Bufo calamita*
Tortoises and turtles:	0	
Lizards:	1-2	*Lacerta vivipara, ?Anguis fragilis*
Snakes:	0	

State of Knowledge

The overall pattern of distribution is known and published on a 10km tetrad map, but only *Bufo calamita* has sufficient detail, on sites and status, for conservation use. *Anguis fragilis* has recently been confirmed from the lowland limestone of the Burren, and its status and origin remain as yet unknown. There was also a small-scale attempt to introduce *Lacerta viridis* into the Burren some 30 years ago. Its survival there and even the location of its release into this large area are not known. However, as all other populations on the northern edge of their range require a sandy substrate for egg-laying and incubation, it must be doubted that the Burren could sustain breeding for long. It has been suggested that *Bufo calamita* also owes its origin to introduction, albeit accidentally, for example in sand ballast from Liverpool Bay. However, its disjunct localities in Kerry do not support this view, and it is more likely to be a

194

member of the noted Lusitanian fauna like the kerry slug, which has a distributional pattern suggesting interglacial survival.

Species Threats

Bufo calamita is very much the rarest and most threatened species. The most recent causes of decline have been land drainage, tourism and pollution.

Almost nothing is known of the situation of *Anguis fragilis* which, if indigenous, may also have a limited range.

Concern has been expressed at the losses of *Triturus vulgaris* breeding waters due to pollution and infilling of gravel pits, but the true extent of the problem remains unknown in the absence of detailed survey. Similarly, the effects of peat extraction on this species and on *Rana temporaria* have yet to be examined.

Conservation Measures Taken

Bufo calamita is strictly protected. Here, habitat protection has been implemented, as shown by recent prosecutions, and by successful opposition against quarry developments. 'Fauna Refuges' have also been established for two of its breeding sites.

Licences are required for the taking or killing of the three commoner species.

Conservation Measures Needed

Much more terrestrial habitat should be incorporated within the two *Bufo calamita* reserves. The Inch sand dunes should be similarly protected and managed. Plans to introduce *B. calamita* into other protected dunes should be pursued to offset site losses elsewhere. Field surveys should be promoted for *Triturus vulgaris* and *Lacerta vivipara* and the results used to develop a site-based conservation strategy. The status of reptiles in the Burren should be investigated, with special consideration given to *Anguis fragilis* and *Lacerta viridis*. Existing Burren reserve boundaries should be considered for amendment so as to incorporate areas of value for reptiles.

Bibliography

Crichton, M. (undated) *Provisional distribution maps of amphibians, reptiles and mammals in Ireland.* Folens An Foras, Forbatha, Dublin.

21
Portugal

Species Summary

Number of indigenous species: 45

Tailed amphibians:	6	*Salamandra salamandra, Chioglossa lusitanica, Pleurodeles waltl, Triturus marmoratus, T. helveticus, T. boscai*
Tailless amphibians:	11	*Discoglossus galganoi, Alytes obstetricans, A. cisternasii, Pelobates cultripes, Pelodytes punctatus, Bufo bufo, B. calamita, Hyla arborea, H. meridionalis, Rana iberica, R. perezi*
Tortoises and turtles:	3	*Emys orbicularis, Mauremys leprosa, Testudo graeca*
Lizards:	14	*Tarentola mauritanica, Hemidactylus turcicus, Chamaeleo chamaeleon, Psammodromus algirus, Podarcis hispanicus, Acanthodactylus erythrurus, Lacerta lepida, L. shreiberi, L. monticola, L. dugesii*, P. hispanica, P. bocagei, Anguis fragilis, Chalcides bedriagai, C. chalcides*
Amphisbaenians:	1	*Blanus cinereus*
Snakes: 10		*Malpolon monspessulanus, Coluber hippocrepis, Elaphe scalaris, Natrix natrix, N. maura, Coronella austriaca, C. girondica, Macroprotodon cucullatus, Vipera seoanei, V. latasti*

*Occurs in Madeira and in the Azores, where it is the only species present.

State of Knowledge

National maps have been compiled for all species of reptiles and amphibians from literature sources, museum and field records. More detailed information exists for amphibians and includes sites and habitat data. The Red Data Book for Portugal confirms the comparative lack of knowledge about the status of many species and concludes that no one species is known to be endangered, but that most are indeterminate or unknown.

Species Threats

The three rarest species are all reptiles. *Chamaeleo chamaeleon* is confined to the south-eastern coastal strip where it is clearly at risk from tourism development, agricultural pressures including pesticide use, and collection. *Lacerta monticola* is confined to montane scrub in the Beira Alta and *Vipera seoanei* is now known only from a handful of localities in the north where it is at risk from habitat loss and persecution.

Five other species with small populations are centred mainly in the north-west, including Beira Alta: *Chioglossa lusitanica, Triturus helveticus, Lacerta shreiberi, Podarcis bocagei* and *Coronella austriaca*. Precise details about the status of and threats to these species are not available but there is concern over the status of breeding ponds for *T. helveticus* and for the unspoilt river and stream valley habitats of *L. shreiberi*.

Drainage, infilling and pollution of small ponds are known to be a major problem for amphibians throughout Portugal. Other significant causes of habitat loss and species decline include the replacement of native woodland by *Eucalyptus* and alien *Pinus* plantations and the deliberate burning of shrubland.

Conservation Measures Taken

Amendments to the national hunting laws are being taken through parliament in an attempt to comply with Portugal's ratification of the Berne Convention. The hunting laws govern hunting of birds and mammals but by omission of any open season for other fauna it is considered that all reptiles and amphibians are protected against

killing or taking. However, there is no real infrastructure for
regional implementation of the law or, more importantly, of habitat
protection, although this situation is currently under review.

Better protection is afforded to those populations which reside in
national parks, providing that wardens can implement adequate
control and providing that appropriate habitat management is
undertaken. Generally speaking, there have not been adequate or
comprehensive assessments of the status and conservation needs of
reptiles and amphibians in national parks. For example, the Peneda-
Geres National Park in northern Portugal supports nine species of
amphibians and 14 reptiles, but their status and population levels are
not known.

The declaration of Berlinga Island as a nature reserve (primarily for
birds) should be recorded as of potential value to insular forms of
Lacerta lepida and *Podarcis bocagei*. Access is strictly limited, and
it is hoped that the needs of these two lizards will be adequately met
within the other aims of this reserve.

Conservation Measures Needed

The rarer and most threatened species should be afforded better
legal protection, with particular attention paid to habitat conservation and management. Where necessary, field research should be
undertaken to determine the actual distribution, status and habitat
associations of the more restricted species, with conservation measures to follow.

Important sites in the Beira Alta and in the key region between
Caminha and Chaves should be protected and managed appropriately. These areas are important as centres of diversity for reptiles
and amphibians within Iberia as a whole, so the identification and
protection of appropriate 'assemblage reserves' is a high priority.

Bibliography

Malkmus, R. (1984) Die Bedeutung der Brunnel für del Anphibien
Bestand Portugas. *Salamandra* 18(3/4): 205-217.
Malkmus, R. (1984) Beiträg zur Verbreitung der Anphibien und Reptilien
in Portugal. *Salamandra* 18(3/4): 218-249.

22
Spain

Species Summary: (i) Mainland Spain and the Balearic Islands

Number of indigenous species: 66

Tailed amphibians:	8	*Salamandra salamandra, Chioglossa lusitanica, Pleurodeles waltl, Euproctus asper, Triturus marmoratus, T. alpestris, T. helveticus, T. boscai*
Tailless amphibians:	16	*Discoglossus galganoi, D. pictus, Alytes obstetricans, A. cisternasii, A. muletensis*, Pelobates cultripes, Pelodytes punctatus, Bufo bufo, B. calamita, B. viridis, Hyla arborea, H. meridionalis, Rana temporaria, R. dalmatina, R. iberica, R. perezi[+]*
Tortoises and turtles:	4	*Testudo hermanni, T. graeca, Emys orbicularis, Mauremys leprosa*
Amphisbaenians:	1	*Blanus cinereus*
Lizards:	24	*Tarentola mauritanica[+], Hemidactylus turcicus[+], Chamaeleo chamaeleon, Algyroides marchi, Psammodromus algirus, P. hispanicus, Acanthodactylus erythrurus, Lacerta lepida, L. schreiberi, L. viridis, L. agilis, L. vivipara, L. monticola, L. perspicillata, Podarcis hispanica, P. muralis, P. bocagei, P. lilfordi*, P. pityusensis*, P. sicula[+], Anguis fragilis, Chalcides bedriagai, C. chalcides, C. pistaciae*

Snakes:	13	*Malpolon monspessulanus, Coluber hippocrepis, C. viridiflavus, Elaphe longissima, E. scalaris[+], Natrix natrix, N. maura[+], Coronella austriaca, C. girondica, Macroprotodon cucullatus[+], Vipera seoanei, V. aspis, V. latastei*

*Endemic to the Balearic Islands.
+Occurs on the mainland and the Balearic Islands.

Species Summary: (ii) Canary Islands

Number of indigenous species: 14

Tailed amphibians:	0	
Tailless amphibians:	2	*Hyla meridionalis, Rana perezi*
Tortoises and turtles:	0	
Lizards:	12	*Tarentola boettgeri, T. delalandii, T. angustimentalis, T. gomerensis, Hemidactylus turcicus, Chalcides sexlineatus, C. viridanus, C. occidentalis, Gallotia atlantica, G. galloti, G.* aff. *simonyi, G. stehlini*
Snakes:	0	

State of Knowledge

There has recently been an increasing awareness of herpetofauna conservation needs in Spain, reflected by the instigation of regional surveys, mapping programmes and ecological research. A Red Data List was published in 1986.

Species Threats

The Spanish Red Data List indicates that 23 species, and a number of subspecies, are threatened. *Alytes muletensis* and *Gallotia simonyi* are endangered by virtue of their rarity and tiny world range. Threats to these species are more fully described in Part Two.

The complex of island populations of *Podarcis lilfordi* and *P. pityusensis* are under threat (see Part Two), and the status of the *Gallotia atlantica* group, notably *G. a. delibesi, G. a. ibagnezi* and *G. a. laurae*, is of similar concern. Three other island lizards with small ranges are *Podarcis hispanica atrata* whose Columbrates refuges are used for military shelling, *Gallotia galloti insulanagae* and *Podarcis muralis rasquinetti*.

Testudo graeca and *T. hermanni* are localised and at risk from habitat loss and from collection. *Chamaeleo chamaeleon* has an even smaller range and is equally at risk from collection.

A number of other species are rare but their precise status is not known. These species are: *Chioglossa lusitanica, Discoglossus galganoi, D. pictus, Bufo viridis balearica, Rana dalmatina, Emys mauremys, Algyroides marchi, Lacerta agilis garzoni, L. monticola, Chalcides occidentalis, C. viridanus, Coluber viridiflavus* and *Elaphe longissima*.

Vipera seoanei and *Lacerta schreiberi* are both confined to northern Spain. Both are at risk from habitat loss but the former species is also subject to persecution.

The main world range of the large and attractive *Lacerta lepida* (Plate 7) is Spain. Although widespread, this species is now declining due to persecution from trapping, shooting and poisoning during the course of game management of red-legged partridge (*Alectoris rufa*). It is also classified as a pest species. *L. lepida* is also caught and eaten and recipes for cooking it are found in national magazines. Agricultural intensification, beginning with simple removal of stone and boulder refuges in fields, is a further pressure upon this species.

A similarly large lizard is *Gallotia stehlini* and this species may be vulnerable due to habitat loss and persecution, although for the time being it is reported to thrive on rubbish tips in the Canary Islands.

Glacial relict populations of *Triturus alpestris* and *Triturus helveticus* are confined to isolated montane ponds and lakes where they could be at risk from hydro-electric schemes, water abstraction, pollution, or the stocking of predatory fish. Populations of the more widespread *Rana iberica*, the Pyrenean *Euproctus asper* and *Triturus boscai* are similarly vulnerable.

Collection remains a problem for the tortoises. Even if confiscated animals are returned to the wild, they usually get caught again or collected for the pet trade. *Chamaeleo chamaeleon* and the fresh-

water terrapins are also subject to collection. Collection for research
or museums is now a matter of concern for a number of threatened
species including *Alytes muletensis, Chamaeleo chamaeleon, Algyroides marchi, Podarcis lilfordi, P. pityusensis* and *Lacerta schreiberi.*

In summary, the main reasons contributing to the decline of Spanish
reptiles and amphibians are:

■ Loss and change of habitats: particularly agricultural intensification, afforestation with *Eucalyptus*, loss and pollution of
freshwaters.

■ Fires (associated with increased tourism or with deliberate
burning for land improvement).

■ Use of pesticides and poisons (these are widely used against
Lacerta lepida and *Gallotia atlantica*).

■ Development on islands (tourism, urbanisation and military
use).

■ Collection for the pet trade.

■ Collection for academic study or museum material.

Conservation Measures Taken

Many species are protected under national legislation dating from
1980. However, a number of threatened species were omitted from
this legislation and, moreover, Spain took several 'reservations'
when they acceded to the Berne Convention. These reservations
included some relatively common species but were based on the
traditional hostility towards salamanders, terrapins, tortoises, geckoes,
L. lepida and poisonous snakes, rather than conservation needs.
There is no national law which protects the habitat of reptiles and
amphibians.

Whilst the species protection legislation is a national matter, it is
implemented at the regional level. The regions vary in their attitudes
and efforts regarding herpetofauna conservation. The situation is
particularly good in the Balearics, Valencia and in the Canary
Islands. In the Balearics, the regional authorities do more than the
minimum required for herpetofauna conservation and have taken
positive action to conserve *Podarcis lilfordi, P. pityusensis* and *Alytes*

muletensis. For the latter species, a number of tadpoles were taken into captivity at Jersey and Stuttgart Zoos to provide captive-breeding stock. These stocks now successfully breed and the first re-introductions to the wild have now taken place. This project aims to augment existing wild populations and to restock past localities for *A. muletensis.* On the island of Hierro (Canary Islands), a sophisti-cated management programme has been instigated to conserve the endangered *Gallotia simonyi.* Measures taken include the removal of goats, predatory cats and dogs and the secure fencing of areas of critical habitat, the building of a large vivarium and hatching facility together with a public viewing and education facility, preparation of sites for re-introduction and employment of a warden.

Conservation Measures Needed

Amendments to the national species protection legislation are required so as to reflect actual conservation needs. Additionally, national legislation is required to ensure adequate protection of the habitats of all threatened species. Until this is done Spain will not be able to implement properly its obligations under the Berne Convention.

The recommendations, as outlined in Part Two and recommended by Standing Committee of the Berne Convention (Appendix I), for *Alytes muletensis, Gallotia simonyi, Podarcis hispanica atrata, P. lilfordi* and *P. pityusensis* require prompt implementation, particu-larly in relation to the need to establish Biogenetic Reserves. This is particularly important in order to remove the threats posed to *Alytes muletensis* from damming and water abstraction schemes, to halt the shelling of *Podarcis lilfordi* habitat on the Cabrera Islands, and to properly implement the *G. simonyi* programme.

A number of new reserves are needed and existing reserves and national parks require boundary modifications in order to include important herpetofauna sites. Such designations are required for glacial pools and lakes in the Pyrenees, Cantabrians, Septentrional and Central mountain regions, and for important herpetofaunal assemblage habitats adjacent to Portugal's Peneda-Geres National Park. Reserves to protect *Chamaeleo chamaeleon, Gallotia atlan-tica, Lacerta schreiberi, Lacerta monticola* and *Vipera seoanei* are also required.

Survey and mapping of reptiles and amphibians in seven million hectares of the Spanish and French Pyrenees has revealed a total of 45 species. These regions therefore have enormous potential for assemblage reserves. Further habitat assessment and options for site protection should be pursued. Additionally, more detailed surveys and habitat assessments are required for some species of indeterminate status.

The unjustified persecution and exploitation of *L. lepida,* arguably the 'flag-ship' species for the conservation of European reptiles and amphibians, must be stopped.

Bibliography

Martinez Rica, J. P. (1983) *Atlas herpetologico del Pirineo,* 35: 1-2, pp.51-80. MUNIBE. Sociedad de Ciencias ARANZADI. San Sebastian.

23
France

Species Summary: (i) Mainland France

Number of indigenous species: 56-57

Tailed amphibians:	9	*Salamandra salamandra, S. atra, Euproctus asper, Triturus marmoratus, T. cristatus, T. alpestris, T. vulgaris, T. helveticus, Speleomantes italicus*
Tailless amphibians:	18	*Bombina variegata, Discoglossus pictus, Alytes obstetricans, Pelobates cultripes, P. fuscus, Pelodytes punctatus, Bufo bufo, B. calamita, B. viridis, Hyla arborea, H. meridionalis, Rana arvalis, R. dalmatina, R. temporaria, R. ridibunda, R.* kl. *esculenta*, R. lessonae, R. perezi*
Tortoises and turtles:	3	*Testudo hermanni, Emys orbicularis, Mauremys leprosa*
Lizards:	14	*Tarentola mauritanica, Hemidactylus turcicus, Phyllodactylus europeaus, Psammodromus algirus, P. hispanicus, Lacerta lepida, L. viridis, L. agilis, L. vivipara, Podarcis muralis, P. hispanica, Chalcides chalcides, Anguis fragilis, Podarcis sicula*
Snakes:	12 -13	*Malpolon monspessulanus, Coluber viridiflavus, Elaphe longissima, E. scalaris, Natrix natrix, N. maura, Coronella austriaca, C. girondica, Vipera ursinii, V. berus, V. seoanei, V. aspis, (?V. latasti)*

Species Summary: (ii) Corsica

Number of indigenous species: 18

Tailed amphibians:	2	*Salamandra corsica*[+], *Euproctus montanus*[+]
Tailless amphibians:	5	*Discoglossus montalentii*[+], *D. sardus, Bufo viridis, Hyla sarda, Rana* kl. *esculenta**
Tortoises and turtles:	2	*Testudo hermanni, Emys orbicularis* , (*Caretta caretta* is probably no longer a breeding species)
Lizards:	7	*Tarentola mauritanica, Hemidactylus turcicus, Phyllodactylus europeaus, Algyroides fitzingeri, Lacerta bedriagae, Podarcis tiliguerta, P. sicula*
Snakes:	2	*Coluber viridiflavus, Natrix natrix cetti*

*The 'hybrid' edible frog is treated as a species.
+Endemic species.

State of Knowledge

An atlas of distribution on a coarse scale is currently being updated. Additionally, the national computer records system of the Secretariat de la Faune et de la Flore holds much more detailed information at a site level. This quite comprehensive data collection has been made possible by government-funded research as part of a regular national census. A Red Data Book was published in 1983.

Species Threats

The Red Data Book lists three mainland reptiles and four amphibians as endangered, with a further ten reptiles and 11 amphibians as declining and vulnerable (the latter category includes three Corsican endemics).

Vipera ursinii is considered as the most endangered species in France. There are nine separate populations in montane meadows in Vaucluse, Alpes de Haute Provence and Alpes Maritimes; none of these sites are protected as nature reserves and several are at risk from skiing activities and developments, including the mechanical creation of piste. Other meadows are dependent on the maintenance of appropriate grazing regimes. All the populations are vulnerable to collection and this has encouraged a policy of maintaining secrecy about the location of the sites, in some cases to the detriment of their conservation.

Although *Testudo hermanni* is not thought to be threatened in Corsica, it is vulnerable to the increasing number of forest and maquis fires associated with increased tourism and which are now progressively degrading the habitat. However, *T. hermanni* is now endangered on the mainland where its range covers only 240km² with a density is as low as three animals per hectare. Forest fires, expansion and intensification of agriculture and urban development into the plains and coastal strips, tourism, road mortalities and former heavy collection have all contributed to the massive contraction in range and decline in numbers of *T. hermanni*. Casual collection continues and the remaining population is threatened by fires, road mortality and other tourist-related pressures. The decline in traditional cutting and grazing of maquis has increased the fire risk and has additionally reduced the availability of open ground necessary for egg-laying and incubation, and also renders remaining nest sites increasingly vulnerable to mammalian predators.

There has also been a significant loss in the habitat of *Emys orbicularis* as a result of land drainage, disturbance of their wintering hibernation sites, and forest fires in southern France which also desiccate streams and associated wetland habitats.

Bombina variegata is declining and considered at risk from changing agricultural practices and the loss of field ponds from neglect, infilling and replacement by troughs.

Three species of amphibians reach the limits of their westerly range in mainland France where they are restricted, declining and threatened. *Bufo viridis* is under threat from drainage of marshes and gravel extraction (although it remains widespread on Corsica); *Rana arvalis* is threatened by land drainage and by stocking of waters by fish; and *Pelobates fuscus* is threatened by sand and gravel extraction and subsequent infilling of pits.

Pelobates cultripes has its eastern range limits in western France where it is mainly confined to coastal dune systems. There its decline has been due to habitat loss from tourism developments, afforestation and wetland drainage for mosquito control.

Three species just penetrate into France via the Pyrenees, making them very rare nationally, but not really under threat nor deserved of any special conservation effort: *Mauremys leprosa, Lacerta monticola* and *Vipera seoanei*. Three other species are potentially vulnerable, being rare and confined to specialised habitats: *Salamandra atra, Speleomantes italicus* and *Triturus alpestris*.

Concern must also be expressed for *Discoglossus sardus* and *Discoglossus montalentii* whose range in Corsica is dependent on a diminishing number of ponds and small lakes, and for *Natrix natrix cetti* in its only French range of Corsica and whose future may be linked with those of its amphibian food. *Phyllodactylus europaeus* is known to be declining throughout its range (see Italy).

Amongst other species known to be declining but not yet thought to be endangered is *Triturus cristatus,* except at its scientifically interesting overlap with *Triturus marmoratus* where decline is due to both loss of breeding ponds and removal of hedges and trees.

Conservation Measures Taken

Although France has not yet ratified the Berne Convention (problems remain over hunting practices), the herpetofauna is protected against killing, injuring, catching, keeping or trade, with the exception of *Vipera berus, V. aspis* and the green frogs. The last exception has recently been restricted to cover only private domestic ponds fished in season for private domestic consumption.

One advantage of the national system is that the Societé Herpetologique de France is given the direct responsibility and funds to advise on conservation needs and enforce legislation, for instance regarding collection, sale and exhibition of native or CITES-listed species.

There is no automatic habitat protection, even for the more endangered species. Nature reserve designation is a lengthy procedure not usually thought appropriate for individual herpetofauna species. A particularly favoured measure for the protection of small sites is the 'Arrêtés de Biotope'. This may be enacted by the Préfet who can make an order to prevent damage to the habitat of a species listed as protected by government. Three recent examples of sites protected in this way are a sand dune site for *Pelobates cultripes,* a quarry for three newt species, a lake supporting a noted assemblage of herpetofauna, and several small sites for *Bombina variegata.*

One current and successful conservation project has been the Station d'Observation et de Protection des Tortues des Maures (SOPTOM), designed to safeguard a core area of the range of *Testudo hermanni* in the Massif des Maures in the south of France. This project incorporates habitat protection and management, captive breeding, reintroduction and public education all aimed at one of France's most endangered herpetofauna species. More than 300 tortoises were recently rescued from the route of a new motorway and transferred to SOPTOM.

The proposal to designate the Port-Cros National Park in the Iles d'Hyeres could conserve stretches of the only national habitats for *Phyllodactylus europaeus* in France outside of Corsica.

Conservation Measures Needed

A better method of habitat protection is required in order to safeguard populations of endangered species and this should be prompted by the ratification of the Berne Convention by France. The system of Arrêté de Biotope is useful under certain circumstances, but can sometimes prove irreconcilable with the rights of private owners.

There should be field conservation assessments with recommendations made to protect the best Corsican sites for *Discoglossus montalentii* and *Discoglossus sardus, Testudo hermanni, Phyllodactylus europeaus, Lacerta bedriagae* and *Natrix natrix cetti.* Prompt action here could well take advantage of conservation opportunities that are already lost to the mainland for species and their habitats. Likewise there should be a re-assessment of the Iles d'Hyeres situation for *Phyllodactylus europeaus* and *Discoglossus sardus* (or possibly *Discoglossus montalentii*) and their conservation needs.

Better site conservation measures and reserve designations are clearly required to maintain *Vipera ursinii's* disjunct range in France;

this could be achieved in part by the extension of an adjacent Biosphere reserve, or via the recommendations for further Biogenetic Reserves. It could be done by publicising only the rare invertebrates on which it feeds or the rare plants amongst which it lives; but some positive steps must be made to improve the precarious situation for this internationally threatened snake.

The SOPTOM project for *Testudo hermanni* should be continued and extended, with priority to the acquisition of further land for protection as nature reserve. Consideration should be given to a site based protection and re-introduction programme for land formerly occupied by the species's core range within the Plaine des Maures.

Nature reserve status and appropriate habitat management should be pursued for large, geographically significant populations of *Bufo viridis, Rana arvalis, Pelobates fuscus* and *Bombina variegata*, wherever possible incorporating a series of breeding waters, as well as the most important dune habitats for *Pelobates cultripes*.

A scientifically important aspect of the French herpetofauna which needs conservation attention is the habitats within the areas of range overlap between each of (a) *Triturus cristatus* and *T. marmoratus* (including sites supporting feral 'Triturus blasii'); (b) *Hyla arborea* and *H. meridionalis*; (c) *Discoglossus montalentii* and *D. sardus*; and (d) *Vipera berus* and *V.aspis*. It is already clear that species are more vulnerable at the edge of their range, but in these foregoing examples it seems that the closely related species concerned are in even less stable circumstances, with habitat changes giving clear advantages to one at the expense of the other. Applied conservation research is needed to resolve their needs.

Bibliography

Société Herpétologique de France. (In press, 1989) *Atlas de Repartition des amphibians et des reptiles de France*. Edité par le Secretariat Faune et Flore avec le concours du Ministère l'Environment. Paris.

24
Monaco

Species Summary

Number of indigenous species: 9

Tailed amphibians:	0	
Tailless amphibians:	3	*Rana* kl. *esculenta*, Bufo bufo, Hyla meridionalis*
Tortoises and turtles:	0	
Lizards:	5	*Podarcis muralis, Lacerta viridis, Tarentola mauritanica, Hemidactylus turcicus, Anguis fragilis*
Snakes:	1	*Coronella girondica*

*The 'hybrid' edible frog is treated as a species.

State of Knowledge

Since the Principality of Monaco is mainly urban, the number of amphibian and reptile species is low. However, a few important herpetofauna localities have been preserved. The nine species named above are observed regularly in the Principality and are a well-established part of the fauna. However, several other species found in the surrounding districts may occur in Monaco, including *Rana dalmatina, Salamandra salamandra, Speleomantes italicus, Elaphe longissima, E. scalaris,* and *Coluber viridiflavus*. Reptiles and amphibians in Monaco are found mainly in the Exotic Garden and other private gardens, the undeveloped areas on the rock of Monaco, and the valley of Saint Devota and other valleys near the Larvotto. Ponds in the Exotic Garden provide sites for anuran eggs and larvae. Although *Coronella girondica* is approaching extinction, *Podarcis muralis* and *Tarentola mauritanica* remain very common throughout the Principality. Thus, in comparison with other urban areas, number of species is surprisingly high.

Species Threats

Apart from *Coronella girondica*, the amphibian and reptile fauna is not threatened.

Conservation Measures Taken and Needed

At present, Monaco has no specific laws for the protection of animals, although it has ratified CITES. However, the green areas, and particularly the known spawning sites in Monaco, benefit from total protection.

A local study and conservation programme should be instituted for *C. girondica*.

25

Switzerland

Species Summary

Number of indigenous species: 32

Tailed amphibians:	7	*Salamandra atra, S. salamandra, Triturus alpestris, T. carnifex, T. cristatus, T. helveticus, T. vulgaris*
Tailless amphibians:	11	*Alytes obstetricans, Bombina variegata, Bufo bufo, B. calamita, Hyla arborea, Rana lessonae, R.* kl. *esculenta*, R. ridibunda, R. dalmatina, R. latastei, R. temporaria*
Tortoises and Turtles:	0	
Lizards:	6	*Anguis fragilis, Lacerta agilis, L. viridis, L. vivipara, Podarcis muralis, P. sicula*
Snakes:	8	*Natrix natrix, N. maura, N. tessellata, Coronella austriaca, Elaphe longissima, Coluber viridiflavus, Vipera aspis, V. berus*

*The 'hybrid' edible frog is treated as a species.

State of Knowledge

The current state of knowledge in Switzerland differs somewhat between amphibians and reptiles. Every Swiss canton has completed a project to survey amphibian breeding sites (a total of 8,000 sites) and a synthesis of these is given in Grossenbacher (1988). The situation concerning amphibians is better known in lowland areas than in the hilly and mountainous regions, and better known in the eastern and central than in the western and southern parts of the country. For reptiles, only small parts of Switzerland are as yet similarly covered, mainly the French speaking parts and the Grisons, in the south-east. In some of the German speaking cantons, survey projects are in progress or about to start, but in the central part of the country there are not even plans as yet. A combined project for the whole of Switzerland cannot be finished within the next five years. Kramer and Stemmler (1986) have produced distribution maps for the reptiles in Switzerland. The general distribution of every species is well documented, but detailed information about habitats, abundance, status and threats are not included.

Species Threats

Pelobates fuscus, Bufo viridis, Rana arvalis and *Emys orbicularis* are now extinct. The three amphibian species occurred only in single populations in the vicinity of the French-Swiss border near Basel and the Italian-Swiss border in the southern Ticino. *Emys orbicularis* was in earlier times widespread in the lowlands, and seems to have disappeared due to climatic changes. Several reintroductions have been tried, but without success.

Salamandra atra, Rana dalmatina, R. latastei, Podarcis sicula, Natrix maura and *Vipera berus* are endangered. Of these, only three populations of *R. latastei* now remain, near the Swiss-Italian border. None of the sites are sufficiently protected, and one is seriously threatened. Only very few populations of *P. sicula* occur, all in the southernmost part of Switzerland. At present it is not clear if the populations are native or were introduced (*P. sicula* is abundant in Italy). There are only a few populations of *N. maura* in the canton of Geneva, along Lake Geneva and the River Rhone. The pure native populations are threatened from hybridisation with introduced *N. maura* and from competition with introduced *N. tessellata*, a species which is already much more abundant in some habitats than is *N. maura*.

Rana dalmatina (north), *Salamandra atra* (central and southern Alps), *Vipera berus* (western and southern Alps) are all very rare in these regions, partly restricted by the unfavourable climate (they have never been much more abundant). Their habitats are now very isolated and need to be strictly protected and appropriately managed.

Vulnerable species are: *Triturus cristatus* (whole area), *T. vulgaris* (west and south), *Hyla arborea* (whole area), *Bufo calamita* (west), *Alytes obstetricans* (west) and *Coronella austriaca* (north). All these species are rare, and have declined in these regions, mainly because of habitat loss.

Conservation Measures Taken

Since 1967 all amphibian and reptile species have been protected in Switzerland, insofar as collecting, killing and trading is forbidden. The protection of their habitats was not sufficiently regulated in this act, however. In 1982 Switzerland ratified the Berne Convention, but its effect at the cantonal level (the cantons are responsible for the protection of nature) was negligible, although the different Swiss cantons have created several hundred areas protected for nature, most of them small in size. The larger areas of several square kilometres are mainly situated in the Alps, where the really endangered species of reptiles and amphibians do not occur. Areas were rarely protected specifically for herpetofauna, but in recent years some pits and small wetlands have been protected mainly because of their amphibian fauna. In 1988, the Federal Act of 1967 on the protection of nature was revised according to the provisions of the Berne Convention to cover habitat protection such that the federal government has to designate and protect habitats of national importance with support from the cantons.

Conservation Measures Needed

Field studies into population dynamics, habitat selection and reasons for decline have rarely been undertaken in Switzerland. Such studies are needed for the above-mentioned endangered and vulnerable species. At present only two investigations are in progress, both into the decline of *Hyla arborea*. Better collaboration with institutes and universities would be helpful.

The highest conservation priority in international terms is the protection of the few remaining habitats of *Rana latastei* in the canton of Ticino, one of the most endangered amphibian species in the European continent. The wetland breeding areas and its terrestrial habitats require appropriate management, and new habitats should be established, where possible. There is also a case for establishing Biogenetic Reserves for those species, which are threatened in other European countries or have restricted distributional ranges, but which are still abundant and form large populations in parts of Switzerland. Such species may include *Salamandra atra, Triturus helveticus, Alytes obstetricans, Bombina variegata, Lacerta agilis* and *Vipera berus*. These reserves must contain one or more of the largest populations of these species.

Mountains hold the most characteristic ecosystems in Switzerland. Several large alpine national parks should be created, where only traditional farming is allowed and where modern tourism is excluded. They should include some of the amphibian and reptile populations which live here under special ecological and climatic conditions: *Triturus alpestris, Bufo bufo, Rana temporaria, Lacerta vivipara, Coronella austriaca, Vipera berus* and *V. aspis*.

The revised act of 1988 for the protection of nature and the completed inventory of amphibian breeding places provide an opportunity for formulating a systematic plan for establishing amphibian reserves. A preliminary network of the most important breeding places covering the whole country has already been defined, using criteria such as number of species, occurrence of rare species and population size, at national and regional levels. This network of nationally important breeding sites numbers around 800 proposed sites (10 per cent of the total recorded). At the moment, another 10 per cent of all recorded breeding places are protected at a cantonal level, but they were not selected under any herpetological criteria. The list should now be endorsed by the federal government and proposed to the cantonal authorities, who have the competence to establish reserves. By these means a relatively large number of populations of rare and endangered species could be protected. The list of all the other breeding places will be sent directly to the cantonal, regional and local authorities.

Because of the lack of a completed reptile inventory, it is not possible to define clear criteria for protection priorities in the same way as for amphibians. Presently, the proposals for reptile reserves are made as individual cases. As soon as reptile surveys are finished in some of the cantons, a similar system can be formulated and applied. Site protection should certainly not wait for completion of projects in all the cantons.

The importation of frogs and frogs-legs is still permitted and although it is forbidden to release imported frogs, enforcement of this is practically impossible. The only workable solution to this problem would be to ban the importation of all species of frogs and frogs-legs for consumption.

Although Switzerland has had a 'Coordination centre for the protection of amphibians and reptiles' for 10 years, coordination and collaboration between herpetologists could be improved. There is still a need for better public awareness, particularly over snake-killing. The typical reptile habitat is in the opinion of most people a wilderness, which should be tidied up. A long term aim is to influence public opinion in a direction such that habitat destruction can be stopped, agriculture 'extensified' and the effects of isolation of natural habitats lessened by creating wildlife corridors and new habitats. The practice of canalising rivers and creeks should be modified to give a more natural effect and the general lowering of the ground water table must be halted. If these general and fundamental reasons for the decline of the herpetofauna cannot be changed in the future, an improvement of the situation in Switzerland will be impossible.

Bibliography

Grossenbacher, K. (1988) *Verbreitungsatlas der amphibien der Schweiz.* Dokumenta Faunistica Helvetiae. Schweiz. Bund für Naturschutz, Basel.

Hotz, H. J. and Broggi, M. F. (1982) *Rote liste der gefährdeten und seltenen amphibien und reptilien der Schweiz.* Schweiz. Bund für Naturschutz, Basel.

Kramer, E. and Stemmler, O. (1986) Schematische verbreitungskarten der Schweizer reptilien. *Revue Suisse Zoologie* 93(3): 779-802.

26
Liechtenstein

Species Summary

Number of indigenous species: 17

Tailed amphibians:	4	*Salamandra atra, Triturus cristatus, T. alpestris, T. vulgaris*
Tailless amphibians:	6	*Bombina variegata, Bufo bufo, Hyla arborea, Rana temporaria, R. lessonae, R. kl. esculenta**
Tortoises and turtles:	0	
Lizards:	4	*Lacerta agilis, L. vivipara, Podarcis muralis, Anguis fragilis*
Snakes:	3	*Natrix natrix, Coronella austriaca, Vipera berus*

*The 'hybrid' edible frog is treated as a species.

In Fürstentum Liechtenstein all amphibians and reptiles, with the exception of *Vipera berus*, are protected under the Nature Conservation Act of 1933. A new act is now being drafted since Liechtenstein has ratified the Berne Convention. The country has nine nature reserves covering an area of 160 ha (1 per cent of the total land surface). The problems of herpetofauna conservation are similar to those in Switzerland Priorities should address the conservation of habitats for *Salamandra. atra, Triturus cristatus, Hyla arborea* and *Vipera berus*.

27
Italy

Species Summary: (i) Mainland Italy

Number of indigenous species: 62

Tailed amphibians:	11	*Salamandra atra, S. salamandra, S. aurorae, Salamandrina terdigitata, Triturus carnifex, T. alpestris, T. vulgaris, T. italicus, Speleomantes ambrosii, S. italicus, Proteus anguinus*
Tailless amphibians:	16	*Bombina variegata, Discoglossus pictus, Alytes obstetricans, Pelobates fuscus insubricus, Pelodytes punctatus, Bufo bufo, B. viridis, Hyla arborea, H. meridionalis, Rana temporaria, R. dalmatina, R. latastei, R. italica, R. kl. esculenta*, R. lessonae, R. ridibunda.*
Tortoises and turtles:	4	*Testudo graeca, T. hermanni, Emys orbicularis, Caretta caretta*
Lizards:	16	*Tarentola mauritanica, Hemidactylus turcicus, Phyllodactylus europaeus, Cyrtopodion kotschyi, Algyroides nigropunctatus, Lacerta horvathi, L. lepida, L. viridis, Podarcis muralis, P. sicula, P. wagleriana, P. filfolensis, P. melisellensis, Anguis fragilis, Chalcides ocellatus, C. chalcides*
Snakes:	15	*Malpolon monspessulanus, Coluber viridiflavus, C. laurenti, Elaphe situla, E. quatuorlineata, E. longissima, Natrix natrix, N. tessellata, Coronella austriaca, C. girondica, Macroprotodon cucullatus, Telescopus fallax, Vipera ursinii, V. aspis, V. ammodytes*

*The 'hybrid' edible frog is treated as a species.

Species Summary: (ii) Sardinia

Number of indigenous species: 26

Tailed amphibians:	5	*Euproctus platycephalus, Speleomantes flavus, S. genei, S. imperialis, S. supramontis*
Tailless amphibians:	3	*Discoglossus sardus, Bufo viridis, Hyla sarda*
Tortoises and turtles:	4	*Testudo hermanni, T. marginata, Emys orbicularis, Caretta caretta* (*T. marginata* is well established but presumed an ancient introduction)
Lizards:	9	*Tarentola mauritanica, Hemidactylus turcicus, Phyllodactylus europeaus, Algyroides fitzingeri, Lacerta bedriagae, Podarcis tiliguerta, P. sicula, Chalcides ocellatus, C. chalcides*
Snakes:	5	*Coluber hippocrepis, C. viridiflavus, Elaphe longissima, Natrix natrix cetti, N. maura*

State of Knowledge

Large-scale national mapping has been undertaken, mainly using existing and museum records rather than special field surveys. However, there has been an increased activity in regional surveys, mostly for amphibians, and with most effort directed towards the rarer species. Some work is also beginning on reptiles, with research, survey and conservation proposals being made for regional populations of *Testudo hermanni* and *Emys orbicularis*. The SEH projects on *Rana latastei, Pelobates fuscus insubricus* and *Vipera ursinii* have furthered knowledge on the distribution and conservation requirements of these species (see Chapter 5).

Species Threats

Mainland Italy

There are ten mainland species in need of special conservation measures because they are seriously threatened or extremely rare. These are *Salamandra aurorae, Speleomantes ambrosii, Proteus anguinus, Pelobates fuscus insubricus, Rana latastei, Caretta caretta, Lacerta lepida, L. horvathi* and *Vipera ursinii*.

Salamandra aurorae is an Italian endemic confined to only two small mountain valleys where it is at risk from uncontrolled collection, not only as an attractive pet, but also for museum specimens. Another endemic, *Pelobates fuscus insubricus*, is elusive in its habits and at risk from breeding pond loss and pollution.

Speleomantes ambrosii was only recently described as a species, known only from a very small area of Florence. This site is not protected, and it could suffer heavy collection owing to its novelty.

Proteus anguinus is a subterranean species confined to limestone cave systems shared with north-west Yugoslavia. Its habitat is reported as suffering from pollution, waste tipping, water abstraction, and from interference from caving activities.

The few surviving nesting beaches of *Caretta caretta* in southern Italy, Sicily and Lampedusa are threatened by unfettered tourist activity and associated developments. Adults and sub-adults are also caught accidentally by fishing fleets engaged mostly in long-line fishing, but also by local fisherman in trawl nets.

Lacerta lepida is now confined to the coastal area of north-west Italy where tourism developments, roads, and maquis fires combine to effect its decline. *L. horvathi* is confined to karst limestone around Trieste where industrial and urban pressures are degrading its habitat.

Five populations of *Vipera ursinii* are confined to montane meadows in five separate regions of the Central Appenines. They are at risk from collection, grazing regime changes and the burning of juniper (*Juniperus* species) by shepherds, and from skiing developments.

It is hoped that the insular race of *Vipera aspis montecristi* is now safe, but it seems certain that the beautiful *Podarcis sicula faraglionensis* is now extinct from its only locality off Capri, due to overcollection, and now shares the same fate as *Podarcis sicula sanctistephani*. Several other noted island races remain at serious risk: *Podarcis muralis meullerlorenzi* and *Podarcis sicula cerbolensis*.

Another 11 species are now giving rise for concern because they appear to be rarer than previously thought and/or because they are known to be declining. *Pelodytes punctatus, Testudo hermanni* (several noted populations no longer breed due to predation from introduced boar and other mammals), *Cyrtopodion kotschyi*, *Phyllodactylus europeaus* (loss of coastal trees such as *Juniperus phoenicea* may be implicated), *Podarcis melisellensis*, *Emys orbicularis*, *Malpolon monspessulanus*, *Telescopus fallax*, *Coluber laurenti*, *Elaphe quatuorlineata* and *E. scalaris*.

Many of the species and habitats in the vast plain of the Po Valley in northern Italy are suffering from the ever increasing pressures of agricultural exploitation and urban and industrial expansion. Apart from the direct loss of natural and semi-natural habitats, the remaining countryside is subjected to gross contamination from pesticides and fertilisers and a general lowering of the water table by over-exploitation for domestic, agricultural and industrial uses.

Other regional problems have stemmed from summer resorts developing along most coastlines together with associated disruption of road links, and the winter sports exploitation of many mountain habitats (for example, there have been recent proposals for extensive ski-runs within the largest *Vipera ursinii* site).

No legislation or controls yet exist for the regional exploitation of reptiles and amphibians collected for the pet trade or educational purposes, such as *Triturus carnifex* and *Lacerta viridis* which are the most heavily traded 'protected' species.

Sardinia

A number of species on Sardinia require conservation, either because of known or potential threat or because they are rare or occupy only a small range as localised endemics.

Caretta caretta has yet to be confirmed as a breeding species in the south-east of the island, but it is at risk from accidental catching around the heavily fished coast and there are reports of deliberate catching and sale of these turtles, mainly for their carapace.

Lacerta bedriagae is confined to a few mountain areas where it has been reported as declining. *Phyllodactylus europaeus* and *Natrix natrix cetti* (an endemic shared with Corsica) have both recently declined. Reasons for the local decline of *P. europeaus* are probably associated with loss of coastal trees, as on the mainland.

Four recently typed cave salamanders (*Speleomantes flavus, S. genei, S. supramontis* and *S. imperialis*) have very small world ranges and habitats that are sensitive to disturbance and pollution, while *Euproctus platycephalus* must be considered vulnerable to habitat destruction from commercial forestry and from increasing demands for water from agriculture and tourism development.

Overgrazing, including the activity of free-ranging pigs, and the results of frequent deliberate or accidental fires are combining to destroy and degrade the remaining reptile habitats on Sardinia. Among the species most at risk are the tortoises *Testudo hermanni* and *T. marginata*.

In addition to the pressures posed by habitat destruction, there do not seem to be any proper controls to prevent private or commercial collection by amateur or professional herpetologists or traders. Until such measures are instituted, collecting poses a dangerous additional pressure, especially on the populations of the rarer species.

Conservation Measures Taken

The national responsibility for species and habitat conservation under the Berne Convention has been devolved to the semi-autonomous regions, without proper guidance or finance. Most regions only have laws relating to hunting and as such their herpetofauna needs are mostly ignored. Exceptions to this are Piemonte, Lombardia and Fruili where recent legislation forbids the capture or killing of all amphibians (except the green frogs) and some reptiles.

Following the change of responsibility for nature conservation from the Ministry of Agriculture and Forestry to the Ministry of Environment, a commission has been set up to try to resolve and improve Berne implementation in the regions. It is hoped that this will greatly benefit Italy's herpetofauna.

Meanwhile, the only habitat protection measure afforded to the herpetofauna is that of national or regional park status, where amphibians and reptiles occur coincidentally within the boundaries of these parks. However, management practices in these areas rarely take account of herpetofauna needs.

Detailed guidance is now being provided for the conservation requirements of herpetofauna in relation to the proposed establishment of a reserve at Mount Nebrodi in Sicily and it is hoped that this might be an example to be followed elsewhere. The National Reserve of Bosco Fontana has proved to be a key site for *Rana latastei*, albeit needing special management and boundary extensions (see Part Two).

Conservation Measures Needed

Proposals for *Rana latastei* and *Vipera ursinii*, detailed in Chapter 4 of this book, and include prompt surveys and implementation of conservation measures for *Vipera ursinii* around Mount Sibillini.

Site oriented proposals for *Pelobates fuscus insubricus* can only be defined by detailed field surveys, although taxonomic assessment would be helpful in determining conservation priority - namely, whether or not these animals are a separate species from those north of the Alps, as has been suggested (see Chapter 4).

Although Italian nesting sites for *Caretta caretta* now support only a few females each at best, not one site has been protected for this endangered species nor have any of the adverse tourist pressures been reduced. It is not unreasonable to propose that each located nest site should be protected each summer from direct human pressure, and that the beaches concerned should be shielded from artificial lighting associated with nearby hotels and tourist facilities during the nesting and hatching season.

Conservation of sites for *Proteus anguinus* is another international priority. The adverse impact of Trieste's industry, particularly with regard to waste disposal and water abstraction, should be assessed and where necessary, controlled. In addition, a biological survey aided by speleologists, should be undertaken as a matter of pressing urgency as an international operation in conjunction with the northwest Yugoslavian authorities.

The range of *Salamandra aurorae* should be protected and guarded against collecting.

The status of the four Sardinian *Speleomantes* species, *S. ambrosii*, *Euproctus platycephalus*, *Phyllodactylus europaeus*, *Lacerta bedriagae* and *Natrix natrix cetti* should be assessed and corresponding assessments made of their habitats and conservation needs, including the designation of protected areas where required.

With further field surveys for reptiles, it should be possible to identify key habitats supporting, for example, a number of the reptile species considered at risk. For instance, such surveys have resulted in the identification of key flora and fauna sites of the karst near Rosandra above Trieste, which support *Algyroides nigropunctatus*, *Podarcis melisellensis*, *Lacerta horvathi* and *Coluber laurenti*.

An species assemblage reserve is recommended for Orosei in southeast Sardinia (see Chapter 5), with a possible extension to Mount Genneargentu so as to encompass one of the main *Lacerta bedriagae* habitats. This should be implemented without further delay, before there is further increase of tourism facilities and urban development.

In terms of national legislation and its implementation, there should be improvement to national laws so that they properly reflect the obligations of the Berne Convention for Appendix II species and their habitats, and permit the control of exploitation of reptiles and amphibians for export. To achieve this it will be necessary to overcome the present system of regional autonomy and replace the narrow hunting legislation provisions by proper enforceable conservation laws. This is acutely needed for Sardinia, in particular, whose unique endemics and relatively unspoilt habitats merit national park and national nature reserve status before their heritage value is squandered needlessly. As the Sardinian economy is poor in comparison with much of mainland Italy, it follows that any conservation proposals must be accompanied by adequate financial aid and recompense to local people.

28
Malta

Species Summary

Number of indigenous species: 9

Tailed amphibians:	0	
Tailless amphibians:	1	*Discoglossus pictus*
Tortoises and turtles:	0	
Lizards:	4	*Tarentola mauritanica, Hemidactylus turcicus, Podarcis filfolensis, Chalcides ocellatus*
Snakes:	4	*Coluber algirus, Coluber viridiflavus, Elaphe situla, Telescopus fallax*

State of Knowledge

The distribution and status of the herpetofauna of Malta and its outlier Gozo is well known. A Red Data Book is to be published in 1989.

Species Threats

Urban development has destroyed and polluted many former herpetofauna habitats on the island of Malta, where many reptiles now tend to occur in semi-urban parks rather than in open countryside.

Lowered water tables and pollution have made breeding waters unsuitable for *Discoglossus pictus*, a species which has experienced a serious decline. The adults and larval stages of this species are also heavily collected by children.

The killing of snakes is a persistent problem and has probably contributed to the extreme rarity of *Coluber algirus* on Malta, where it is considered endangered. Malta is its only European location.

Although there is no breeding population of *Caretta caretta* remaining on Gozo's beaches, Malta is the only European country that deliberately exploits it. They are caught for food and for their shells, and fished for 'sport'. Returned tags are witness to resultant losses from both the Greek and the remnant Italian populations.

Other endangered species are *Elaphe situla* and *Telescopus fallax* which are both confined to the main island of Malta.

Chamaeleo chamaeleon deserves a mention since it is rare in Europe, but can be found in scattered places on Malta following its accidental introduction there 100 years ago. It is subject to unrestricted collection for the pet trade.

Conservation Measures Taken

No conservation measures have been taken for Maltese reptiles and amphibians. However, a new nature conservation law is currently being drafted and it is anticipated that some protection will then be afforded to them.

The protection and access restrictions afforded to the small island of Filfla has benefited *Podarcis filfolensis*.

The National Bird Sanctuary of Buskett Gardens is now an important site for *Discoglossus pictus*.

Conservation Measures Needed

Protective legislation is required, but especially for *Discoglossus pictus, Caretta caretta, Chamaeleo chamaeleon* and all four snakes. The main surviving locality of *Coluber algirus* at Valletta should be protected and managed to conserve and enhance its population.

The best breeding sites for *Discoglossus pictus* should be protected and every opportunity taken to recreate suitable breeding habitat, where possible in conjunction with other safeguarded sites.

The various island forms of *Podarcis filfolensis* should studied and conservation measures enacted to take into account their scientific value, particularly with respect to their potential for speciation.

Nature reserves ought to be declared in unspoilt countryside areas of the island of Gozo before urban and agricultural pressures destroy remaining areas of interest. Priorities for action on Gozo include the conservation of populations of *Podarcis filfolensis gozo, Chalcides ocellatus* and the melanic form of *Coluber viridiflavus*. There are also recent but unconfirmed records for *Elaphe situla* and *Telescopus fallax* and further survey could similarly identify priority conservation areas for these species if they do indeed exist on Gozo.

29
Austria

Species Summary

Number of indigenous species: 34

Tailed amphibians:	7	*Salamandra salamandra, S. atra, Triturus cristatus, T. carnifex, T. dobrogicus, T. alpestris, T. vulgaris*
Tailless amphibians:	13	*Bombina bombina, B. variegata, Pelobates fuscus, Bufo bufo, B. calamita, B. viridis, Hyla arborea, Rana temporaria, R. arvalis, R. dalmatina, R. ridibunda, R. lessonae, R. kl. esculenta**
Tortoises and turtles:	1	*Emys orbicularis*
Lizards:	6	*Lacerta viridis, L. agilis, L. horvathi, L. vivipara, Podarcis muralis, Anguis fragilis*
Snakes:	7	*Elaphe longissima, Natrix natrix, N. tessellata, Coronella austriaca, Vipera (ursinii) rakosiensis, V. berus, V. ammodytes*

*The 'hybrid' edible frog is treated as a species.

State of Knowledge

A Red List of Austrian herpetofauna was published in 1983 and listed 31 species as endangered, *Vipera (ursinii) rakosiensis* as extinct and *Bufo calamita* as 'threatened by extinction'. This Red List was based on distribution data published separately as an Atlas in 1985 which compiled existing records on a broad scale of 100 kilometre squares, with some anomalies and gaps checked in the field. This survey led to the recent discovery of populations of *Lacerta horvathi*.

The Vienna Museum is currently undertaking further surveys in order to update and publish maps for two or three species each year.

Some of the länder have carried out more detailed studies. For instance, the Lände of Vienna has been mapped in detail and this information is now used by the local administration for assessing all new developments.

Species Threats

Vipera (ursinii) rakosiensis is highly endangered throughout its world range and is approaching extinction in Austria due to habitat loss, inappropriate management of its few remaining meadows, past persecution (a bounty system used to exist) and collection for vivaria in recent years. The presence of this species has not been conclusively confirmed in Austria since 1976. No conservation measures have been undertaken for this species, although one site is now receiving attention following the CoE Recommendation of 1988 (see Appendix I).

Bufo calamita is entirely confined to an ancient sand quarry in the north-east where it has been granted a temporary 10-year reprieve from a plan for infilling.

Emys orbicularis is confined to a handful of sites in eastern Austria although there may be undiscovered relict populations, for example in riverine forest. Whether its past localities around Lake Neusiedl were natural or old introductions is not known. However, their loss there and in the Hansag may be linked to pesticides, collection and increasing tourism pressures. These threats are particularly serious as this is a species which is on the edge of its climatic range in Austria. The future existence of *Emys orbicularis* in Austria might depend upon regular restocking from captive sources.

The Danubian form *Lacerta vivipara pannonica* is now very localised in a few remaining damp meadows south of Vienna and at Lake Neusiedl where it is at risk of extinction as a result of intensive agriculture and land drainage.

Natrix tessellata continues to decline as its river refuges succumb to canalisation and other works, disturbance and pollution.

Lowland amphibians are particularly threatened by loss and pollution of breeding waters, with *Triturus dobrogicus* and *Hyla arborea* thought to be particularly vulnerable. *H. arborea* is also collected.

Several species are naturally rare or localised. The status of *Rana arvalis* is not sufficiently known. *Lacerta horvathi* has a highly specialised moist montane habitat and although it does not seem to be currently at risk, it could conceivably be affected by small-scale hydroelectric schemes.

Lacerta viridis is declining as a result of habitat loss due to agriculture. *Podarcis muralis* and *Vipera ammodytes* are both declining due to afforestation, while *V. ammodytes* is also suffering from collection.

Conservation Measures Taken

Nature conservation is the responsibility of the Länder. There is not yet any national nature conservation legislation despite the fact that Austria claims to implement the Berne Convention. The conservation laws of the länder may theoretically protect amphibians and reptiles from collection, disturbance or destruction of breeding habitats. However, other aspects of the länder administration often legally circumvent these protective provisions. Additionally, there is rarely enforcement or implementation of the laws to protect herpetofauna. As a result, in the Tyrol, for example, a few individuals of all species may be kept as pets; in Styria three species of newts, two frogs and the two vipers are excluded from protection; Upper Austria affords only partial protection to *Vipera berus* and *Natrix natrix;* Burgenland omits *Rana esculenta* and *Emys orbicularis* as protected species and continues to allow destruction of *Vipera (ursinii) rakosiensis* habitats through agricultural practices; Carinthia does not protect either *Pelobates fuscus* or *Lacerta horvathi.*

No major herpetofauna reserves have been established. A few threatened species happen to occur within a small number of small reserves, for example: *Podarcis muralis, Lacerta viridis* and *Vipera ammodytes*, but no strongholds of threatened species are covered by Austria's current major proposals for national parks. A number of less threatened montane species occur within the area proposed as the National Park of Hohe Tauern.

Conservation Measures Needed

Species protection should be controlled at a national level to take proper account of national and international priorities and obligations. In particular, national laws should be drafted and implemented to ensure adequate habitat and species protection in accord with the obligations of the Berne Convention, and particularly those of Appendix II relating to protected reptiles and amphibians. This would not only require changes in current legislation but much improved guidance and financing for implementation by the Länder.

Special measures are urgently needed to protect and manage *V. (u.) rakosiensis* habitat better and to undertake detailed surveys of possible sites for this species (see Chapter 4). Similar surveys should be completed for *Emys orbicularis*, together with the production of a species recovery plan. A further survey priority is to identify important breeding sites and enact conservation of important sites for *Triturus dobrogicus, Hyla arborea, Rana arvalis, Lacerta vivipara pannonica* and *Natrix tessellata.*

Known strongholds for *Lacerta viridis, Podarcis muralis* and *Vipera ammodytes* should be included within all relevant national parks with nature reserve status afforded where necessary.

There should be close liaison within Carinthia over any proposed changes or development of the local and sensitive area holding *Lacerta horvathi.*

The single *Bufo calamita* site should be permanently protected and managed.

Bibliography

Cabela, A. and Tiedemann, F. (1985) *Atlas der amphibien und reptilien Österreichs*. Neue Denkschriften des Naturhistorischen Museums in Wien, 4. Bd.

Grillitsch, B. (1985) Der schutzstatus der heimischen amphibien und reptilien. *Ögh-Nachrichten* 3: 13-16.

Häupl, M. and Tiedemann, F. (1983) Rote liste der in Österreich gefährdeten kriechtiere (Reptilia) und lurche (Amphibia). In: Gepp, J. (ed.), *Rote listen gefährdeter tiere Österreichs*. Vienna: Ministry for Health and Environmental Protection.

30
Hungary

Species Summary

Number of indigenous species: 32

Tailed amphibians:	5	*Salamandra salamandra, Triturus cristatus, T. dobrogicus, T. alpestris, T. vulgaris*
Tailless amphibians:	12	*Bombina bombina, B. variegata, Pelobates fuscus, Bufo bufo, B. viridis, Hyla arborea, Rana arvalis, R. dalmatina, R. temporaria, R.* kl. *esculenta*, R. lessonae, R. ridibunda*
Tortoises and turtles:	1	*Emys orbicularis*
Lizards:	7	*Anguis fragilis, Lacerta agilis, L. viridis, L. vivipara, Podarcis muralis, P. taurica, Ablepharus kitaibelii*
Snakes:	7	*Coluber caspius, Coronella austriaca, Elaphe longissima, Natrix natrix, N. tessellata, Vipera berus, V. (ursinii) rakosiensis*

*The 'hybrid' edible frog is treated as a species.

State of Knowledge

The distribution of the six rarest species (all reptiles) is relatively well known at site level, although more detailed information is needed for *Coluber caspius* and for possible surviving pockets of *Vipera (ursinii) rakosiensis*. For the remaining species there have

235

been no comprehensive field surveys. However a mapping scheme began in 1989, using a large 100km tetrad.

Species Threats

The glacial relict populations of *Lacerta vivipara pannonica* now survive at only a few sites in the meadows of the Danube floodplain. It is a victim of agricultural intensification.

Ablephanus kitaibelii inhabits limestone hills to the north of the Danube, as well as several isolated and unusual puszta localities. Its limestone refuges are being lost to summer homes and market gardens which are rapidly encroaching upon the southern scarps within reach of Budapest. Elsewhere, a succession to scrub and afforestation projects are reducing the available open habitat required by the species.

Podarcis taurica is confined to the dry sandy dunes of the south-western Great Plain. Many of these dunes, have now been destroyed by intensive agriculture or, even in the Kiskunsag, planted with trees or converted to orchards.

Coluber caspius needs a much larger territory than other Hungarian reptiles. It is confined to the limestone hills and appears to have suffered even more than *Ablephanus kitaibelii*, and is now considerably rarer. Its size renders it susceptible to a degree of (unlawful) persecution by man.

Vipera berus is now mostly confined to the north-east and to lowland habitats in the south-west. Overall it has suffered from a combination of habitat loss to agriculture and forestry and from human persecution. The predominantly melanic subspecies *V. b. bosniensis* is reputed (with some degree of justification) to be amongst the most venomous and dangerous of the *berus* group, and so it may have been the more difficult to protect. Its national decline now necessitates some remedial action.

Vipera (ursinii) rakosiensis is by far the most endangered of all the Hungarian herpetofauna. It is nearly extinct across the rest of its world range in Austria and Romania and the conservation of this species has become an international priority (see Chapter 4).

Conservation Measures Taken

Hungary was one of the first European countries to enact legislation to protect wild species, with its herpetofauna protected as early as 1947. Under current law, penalties can be imposed for infringements of the law against each species on an increasing scale relating to their rarity and/or perceived value, with certain exceptions (e.g. the poisonous *Vipera berus* and for green frogs). These penalties vary from 500 Forints per specimen to 10,000 Forints for *Vipera (ursinii) rakosiensis* and *Ablepharus kitaibelii* and 30,000 Ft for *Coluber caspius*. However, the 10,000 Ft penalty is not sufficient to prevent habitat destruction, although the presence of these species may sometimes lead to some degree of site protection.

In 1988, following a joint government/SEH field investigation, the fine for harming *V. (u.) rakosiensis* was raised to 30,000 Ft, one of two such 'strictly protected' levels. This level also affords a degree of site protection with, for example, access and any new usage controlled. It is not yet clear whether this will promote habitat management measures or a reversal of habitat destruction. Conservation measures are being applied to the surviving meadows of the Little Plain and its reclaimed Hansag, an area which supports the last known population of *V. (u.) rakosiensis* in western Hungary, as well as a varied amphibian population.

The famous Kiskunsag in the Great Plain covers large areas of puszta (steppe) habitats, maintained as cultural reserves and also partly serving as tourist attractions. Although, this area has been designated a Biosphere Reserve, its 'traditional farming' and tourist uses are not always helpful for herpetofauna conservation, and some of the most important faunal communities lie in meadows outside its borders. Nonetheless, the Bugac and Fulophaza have valuable dune habitats that are important for reptiles, and many amphibians thrive in the damper meadows with ten different species at Lake Kolon alone.

In common with many other countries, military training areas now harbour some of the least altered lowland habitats and support large populations of plains reptiles. These areas are less susceptible to modern agricultural practices and access is restricted. With current plans for international troop reductions, there may be a unique opportunity to protect some of these areas as nature reserves before they are irreversibly destroyed by modern agriculture.

Two noted areas for *Vipera berus* have now been protected in south-west and north-east Hungary. A detailed ecological assessment has just been completed for the important reptile habitat of the limestone scarp near Villany.

Conservation Measures Needed

More reserves must be established and managed for the remaining *V. (u.) rakosiensis* populations, including the few discrete sites in military training areas. There should also be a survey of all suitable habitats within its recently known range, as soon as possible.

Reserves for *Coluber caspius* should be established, particularly in the Villany Hills, an area renowned for rare plants, as well as for its exceptional abundance of lizards. Mineral exploitation should be halted here in deference to the high wildlife importance of the area. In other limestone areas, plans should be devised for maintaining and enhancing reptile habitats, especially for *Ablepharus kitaibelii* and *C. caspius*.

There is still some scope for increasing the diminished range and status of *Podarcis taurica*. Detailed mapping should be undertaken to identify remaining dune ridge populations and adjacent potential habitats which could be restored by successive thinning of poplar and pine plantations, and by the cessation of small scale cultivation of maize and sunflowers. A network of dry dunes linked by corridors could be easily planned and achieved, for example in the remaining areas of the old pusztas Peszeradacs and Baracs, between Dabas and Fulophaza. This would also benefit the unusual reticulate form of *Lacerta viridis,* as well as other noted animals.

While the problems of conserving *Vipera berus bosniensis* may be more difficult to pursue, its protection needs are real and increasing, though any site protection should be preceded by adequate field surveys to update population status data and to confirm habitat associations.

31
Yugoslavia

Species Summary

Number of indigenous species: 64-65

Tailed amphibians:	8	*Salamandra salamandra, S. atra, Triturus carnifex, T. dobrogicus, T. karelinii, T. alpestris, T. vulgaris, Proteus anguinus*
Tailless amphibians:	15	*Bombina variegata, B. bombina, Pelobates fuscus, P. syriacus, Bufo bufo, B. viridis, Hyla arborea, Rana temporaria, R. arvalis, R. dalmatina, R. latastei, R. graeca, R. ridibunda, R. lessonae, R.* kl *esculenta**
Tortoises and turtles:	4	*Testudo hermanni, T. graeca, Emys orbicularis, Mauremys caspica*
Lizards:	20	*Tarentola mauritanica, Hemidactylus turcicus, Cyrtopodion kotschyi, Algyroides nigropunctatus, Lacerta viridis, L. trilineata, L. agilis, L. vivipara, L. horvathi, L. mosorensis, L. oxycephala, L. praticola, Podarcis muralis, P. melisellensis, P. sicula, P. taurica, P. erhardii, Anguis fragilis, Ophisaurus apodus, Ablepharus kitaibelii*
Snakes:	17 -18	*Typhlops vermicularis, Eryx jaculus, Malpolon monspessulanus, Coluber najadum, C. viridiflavus, C. laurenti, C. caspius, Elaphe situla, E. quatuorlineata, E. longissima, Natrix natrix, N. tessellata, Coronella austriaca, Telescopus fallax, Viper ursinii, V. berus, (V. aspis?), V. ammodytes*

*The 'hybrid' edible frog is treated as a species.

State of Knowledge

The national herpetofauna has not been thoroughly studied, either systematically, or with respect to conservation needs. Some regions are better known than others, but much of the country remains poorly surveyed. Istria and the Adriatic coastline, together with other other coastal mountains, have received the most recent attention. Work in most other regions is patchy and is several decades old.

Species or populations of special conservation interest are in most cases located in the coastal area and adjacent mountains and upland lakes; most species occurring over the remainder of the country are widespread in Europe. Further surveys, and systematic work (on isolated upland populations, for example), can be expected to change the current conception of conservation priorities, but the probable magnitude of such change cannot be assessed.

Species Threats

There is no national Red Data Book or similar list of threatened species. However, the taxa listed below can be considered as threatened at the national level.

Proteus anguinus is one of the most endangered species in Europe. It is almost endemic to Yugoslavia, just reaching into the karst zone in the extreme north-east of Italy. It is restricted to subterranean watercourses and is threatened by collection, and probably by reported heavy metal and other pollution of the species's subterranean aquatic habitats, due to recent industrial developments. The exact status of *P. anguinus* remains uncertain due to the difficulty of surveying its habitat.

Triturus vulgaris is a widespread European species with several populations in Yugoslavia, some restricted in distribution. However, only *T. v. schreiberi* currently appears to be declining, from drainage of its habitats.

Bombina variegata kolombatovici is an endemic subspecies confined to the Dalmatian area.

Rana latastei is present in a small area of Istria, north-west Yugoslavia, where it is of restricted distribution and actively threatened by the destruction of riverine forest.

Yugoslavia includes a significant part of the range of *Testudo hermanni*. It has been subject to heavy exploitation for the live animal trade, and is still collected for this purpose in many parts of Yugoslavia.

The upland form *Vipera ursinii ursinii* occurs at several sites along the coastal mountains but has been affected by collection and its status in Yugoslavia is poorly known. The population formerly present on Krk Island seems to have been extirpated by oil development.

It should also be noted that the following taxa have populations that are endemic or nearly endemic to Yugoslavia: *Salamandra atra prenjensis, Lacerta horvathi, L. mosorensis, L. oxycephala, Podarcis melisellensis* and *Algyroides nigropunctatus.*

Conservation Measures Taken

There is no national legislation protecting amphibians and reptiles. However, in the Republic of Slovenia, *Proteus anguinus, Emys orbicularis* and *Mauremys caspica rivulata* are nominally protected, and legislation covering 21 additional species is under consideration.

Conservation Measures Needed

The distribution and status of *Proteus anguinus* needs urgent investigation. Currently available data requires collation and dissemination, and further work should be carried out to determine population trends and the degree to which this species is threatened.

Research is required to ascertain the distribution and status of the numerous endemic and near-endemic taxa which occur along the coast and in adjacent mountains, and to make recommendations for new protected areas where appropriate. This should cover the lacertid lizards cited above, also *Vipera ursinii* and the distinct upland populations of *Triturus*.

The threat posed by the live animal trade and other forms of commercial collection requires investigation. Based on the results, recommendations for appropriate legislative or other action should be made. Emphasis should be on obtaining information about the collection of endemic or near-endemic taxa, and *Testudo hermanni*.

32
Romania

Species Summary

Indigenous species: 43

Tailed amphibians: 6 *Salamandra salamandra, Triturus cristatus, T. dobrogicus, T. alpestris, T. montandoni, T. vulgaris*

Tailless amphibians: 13 *Bombina variegata, B. bombina, Pelobates fuscus, P. syriacus, Bufo bufo, B. viridis, Hyla arborea, Rana temporaria, R. arvalis, R. dalmatina, R.* kl. *esculenta*, R. lessonae, R. ridibunda*

Tortoises and turtles: 3 *Testudo hermanni, T. graeca, Emys orbicularis*

Lizards: 10 *Eremias arguta, Lacerta viridis, L. trilineata, L. agilis, L. vivipara, L. praticola, Podarcis muralis, P. taurica, Anguis fragilis, Ablepharus kitaibelii*

Snakes: 12 *Eryx jaculus, Coluber caspius, Elaphe quatuorlineata, E. longissima, Natrix natrix, Natrix tessellata, Coronella austriaca, Vipera (ursinii) rakosiensis⁺, V. (ursinii) renardi, V.* aff. *rakosiensis/renardi, V. berus, V. ammodytes*

*The 'hybrid' edible frog is treated as a species.
⁺Presumed extinct.

243

State of Knowledge

Work by the late Fuhn and Vancea had by 1982 resulted in the compilation of data on all known localities for each species. This was later updated by field surveys for the rarer species, but the results have not been published and may well have been overtaken by rapid habitat changes which have adversely affected many species, particularly in the lowlands.

Species Threats

At least 18 species were known to be at risk in the early 1980s and the situation for wildlife has generally worsened since then.

Pelobates syriacus and *Rana dalmatina* are localised species threatened by ploughing, pollution and drainage of their habitats. *Triturus dobrogicus* is likely to become endangered in the near future if the drainage, pollution and infilling of its ponds in the Danube Delta continues. *Rana lessonae* also has its largest populations within the Delta and it is declining there for the same reasons as *Triturus dobrogicus*, as well as being threatened by overfishing, particularly during the hibernation period.

The Carpathian endemic *Triturus montandoni* is declining through pollution, drainage and infilling of breeding pools particularly in the Prahova valley. Similarly, breeding sites of *Rana arvalis* are being lost to drainage and pollution of marshes and ponds.

The tortoises continue to be killed by villagers, despite legal protection, and are also declining due to habitat loss and modification.

Ablepharus kitaibelii and *Lacerta praticola* are both considered at risk from intensive spraying of pesticides along their forest-edge habitats.

Eremias arguta has been lost from four of its nine localities while the remaining populations are at risk from tourist development, heavy human pressure, afforestation of sand dunes and pheasant rearing.

Lacerta trilineata (*dobrogica*) is thought to be approaching extinction from human pressure and from habitat loss due to intensive agriculture and urbanisation, for example at the well-known locality of Elena Pavel.

Eryx jaculus is at the northern limit of its range. This factor, and its secretive habits, may account for its apparent disappearance; it was last recorded in 1937 from three localities.

Habitat loss due to agricultural intensification and urbanisation have contributed to the current rarity of *Elaphe quatuorlineata*, though the most immediate threat to this entirely harmless species would seem to be deliberate killing by man. A similar threat faces *Vipera ammodytes*, which has also suffered as a result of the construction of the Portile de Fier hydroelectric scheme that flooded 20 per cent of its known localities.

Perhaps the gravest problem concerns the *Vipera ursinii* group, whose taxonomy is being reviewed. *Vipera (ursinii) rakosiensis* is presumed extinct due to ploughing of its *Stipa* meadow localities. The intermediate form (still being typed at a new specific level), *Vipera aff. rakosiensis/renardi*, has a known world population confined to a meadow reserve of only 50ha that is surrounded on all sides by a vast arable monoculture.

Vipera (ursinii) renardi still has populations within the sand banks and islands of the Danube Delta, but the increasing human disturbance, pollution and activities such as intensive rearing of pheasants pose increasing threats.

Romanian herpetologists have been concerned about the future of a number of localised forms or subspecies thought to be at risk. It is not possible to comment at this stage on the ecological or taxonomic strengths of these, but the animals most threatened are: *Triturus vulgaris empelensis, Lacerta agilis euxinica* (another Danube Delta reptile), *L. a. chersonensis* (declining due to agriculture and the urban expansion of Bucuresti) and *Vipera ammodytes montandoni* (declining due to agriculture, persecution and pheasant rearing).

Conservation Measures Taken

Only two species are known to be protected as 'Monuments of Nature': *Testudo graeca* and *Testudo hermanni*. The forest reserves of Babadag, Slaga Rusa, Hagieni and Atmagea are thought to benefit *T. hermanni*. The dune reserve of Hanu Conachi is very important for the endangered *Eremias arguta*.

All species living in designated forest areas are covered by laws which afford protection to forest fauna, but the effectiveness of these laws is not known and no special conservation measures for forest-living reptiles and amphibians have been reported.

Conservation Measures Needed

Some field survey is required to reassess the status of sites and populations, but the application of conservation measures is more urgent. Legislation is needed to reduce direct persecution of the rarer snakes and the tortoises. Such legislation should be accompanied by an appropriate public awareness campaign. The fishing of hibernating frogs, as well as their collection for export, should be controlled.

Immediate needs include the establishment of nature reserves in the Danube Delta to include Caraorman and Saraturi; the Sadova and Nemira Lakes; the Ciuperceni dunes, and Mount Tutuiatul. If it is not already too late, a buffer zone around the only *Vipera* aff. *rakosiensis/renardi* site needs to be created by pushing back the surrounding intensive agricultural land to create a minimum core area of 100ha and a buffer zone free from pesticide application.

None of this will be easy in an isolated country undergoing intensive economic change which so far appears to have overlooked its natural heritage.

33
Bulgaria

Species Summary

Indigenous species: 50

Tailed amphibians:	5	*Salamandra salamandra, Triturus dobrogicus, T. karelini, T. alpestris, T. vulgaris*
Tailless amphibians:	12	*Bombina variegata, B. bombina, Pelobates fuscus, P. syriacus, Bufo bufo, B. viridis, Hyla arborea, Rana temporaria, R. dalmatina, R. graeca, R.* kl. *esculenta*, R. ridibunda*
Tortoises and turtles:	4	*Testudo hermanni, T. graeca, Emys orbicularis, Mauremys caspica*
Lizards:	13	*Cyrtopodion kotschyi, Ophisops elegans, Lacerta viridis, L. trilineata, L. agilis, L. vivipara, L. praticola, Podarcis muralis, P. taurica, P. erhardii, Anguis fragilis, Ophisaurus apodus, Ablepharus kitaibelii*
Snakes:	16	*Typhlops vermicularis, Eryx jaculus, Malpolon monspessulanus, Coluber najadum, C. rubriceps, C. caspius, Elaphe situla, E. quatuorlineata, E. longissima, Natrix natrix, N. tessellata, Coronella austriaca, Telescopus fallax, Vipera ursinii, V. berus, V. ammodytes*

*The 'hybrid' edible frog is treated as a species.

State of Knowledge

Comprehensive field surveys have not been undertaken, but most of the localities for the rarer species are known. The available data allowed the inclusion of 14 species of reptiles and amphibians in the national Red Data Book published in 1983. Some key habitats of high conservation value for reptiles and amphibians have also been identified and conservation measures proposed.

Species Threats

Coluber rubriceps is a rare species confined mainly to a few Black Sea coastal localities. Its rocky hillside habitat may not be directly at risk from adjacent tourism developments but the increased public pressure and increase in general infrastructure are causes for concern.

The current rarity of *Eryx jaculus* reflects the impacts of foreign snake collectors, who also threaten local populations of colubrids, and *Malpolon monspessulanus.*

Triturus alpestris is naturally confined to relict populations in montane localities. Its ponds are at risk from changing agriculture and forestry practices. *T. dobrogicus* is restricted to the wetlands of the Danube valley where agricultural reclamation, drainage and pesticide use are causing habitat damage. These factors also threaten *Emys orbicularis* and *Mauremys caspica* which are persecuted by fishermen as well.

Very substantial numbers of green frogs are gathered for export each year and although this is not yet considered to have had any demonstrable affects on *Rana ridibunda*, it is thought that further investigation into this is required before an accurate impact statement can be made.

The increasing practice of replacing native deciduous forest by conifers is causing predictable declines in species such as *Salamandra salamandra* and *Elaphe longissima.*

Conservation Measures Taken

Improved legislation was passed in 1986, protecting some 31 species of reptiles and amphibians, with penalties on a sliding scale up to a maximum of 300 Leva for the most endangered. There are as yet no laws to ensure habitat protection for reptile and amphibian species, although many species incidentally occur within the 90 national nature reserves.

Much emphasis has been placed on species protection. There has been media coverage of reptile issues and educational campaigns, which have greatly improved the situation regarding the former widespread killing of snakes, the collection and smuggling of many species and the frequent killing of tortoises for food and use in medicinal folk-lore. Great credit must be given to the recent reversal of pressures on tortoises, including the closure of tortoise restaurants, the cessation of their mass collection and transport, and an end to their public consumption.

Conservation Measures Needed

The field status of *Coluber rubriceps* needs careful study, with the best populations protected in reserves. Protected areas are also urgently needed for the remaining sand dune and semi-desert habitats of *Eryx jaculus*. Similarly, *Triturus alpestris* sites should be safeguarded by the protection of breeding ponds and surrounding habitat.

There appears to be much scope for the inclusion of large populations of *Mauremys caspica*, and amphibian habitats, within general wetland reserves established to encompass some of the unspoilt swamps and marshes remaining in the southern lowlands, and such a policy should be pursued.

Bulgaria's varied and under-developed countryside still presents good opportunities for the designation of 'Assemblage Reserves' which would encompass the representative Balkan herpetofauna. Reserves for habitats rich in tortoises and the larger snakes are particularly recommended, but can only be advanced after the completion of thorough field investigations, which are as yet lacking.

The successful initiative of increasing public awareness of reptile conservation should be continued and consolidated, and used as a positive example for all neighbouring countries which face similar problems over persecution of their native reptiles and amphibians.

34
Greece

Species Summary

Number of indigenous species: 68

Tailed amphibians:	5	*Salamandra salamandra, Mertensiella luschani, Triturus cristatus, T. alpestris, T. vulgaris*
Tailless amphibians:	10	*Bombina variegata, B. bombina, Pelobates syriacus, Bufo bufo, B. viridis, Hyla arborea, Rana epeirotica, R. dalmatina, R. graeca, R. ridibunda*
Tortoises and turtles:	6	*Testudo hermanni, T. graeca, T. marginata, Emys orbicularis, Mauremys caspica, Caretta caretta*
Lizards:	24	*Tarentola mauritanica, Hemidactylus turcicus, Cyrtopodion kotschyi, Stellio stellio, Chamaeleo chamaeleon, Algyroides nigropunctatus, A. moreoticus, Ophisops elegans, Lacerta viridis, L. danfordi, L. trilineata, L. agilis, L. graeca, Podarcis muralis, P. taurica, P. erhardii, P. peloponnesiaca, P. milensis, Anguis fragilis, Ophisaurus apodus, Ablepharus kitaibelii, Chalcides ocellatus, Mabuya aurata, Ophiomorus punctatissimus*
Amphisbaenians:	1	*Blanus strauchi*
Snakes:	21	*Typhlops vermicularis, Eryx jaculus, Malpolon monspessulanus, Coluber najadum, C. laurenti, C. nummifer, C. caspius, C. jugularis* (only on Rhodes), *Elaphe situla, E. quatuorlineata, E. longissima, N. natrix, N. tessellata, Coronella austriaca, Telescopus fallax, Eirenis modesta, Vipera ursinii, V. berus, V. ammodytes, V. schweizeri, V. xanthina*

250

State of Knowledge

There has been no national mapping scheme for herpetofauna and consequently no Red Data assessment. *Caretta caretta* nesting beaches are being investigated and longer term ecological research has been instigated on Zakynthos and Cephalonia. The SEH has investigated the status of *Vipera schweizeri* and *Podarcis milensis* in the western Cyclades (see Part Two). Research has also been completed on some of the many island populations of *Podarcis erhardii*. Most field information has been collected by non-Greek herpetologists. A recent survey added *Vipera ursinii* and *Lacerta agilis* to the Greek species list.

Species Threats

Caretta caretta and *Vipera schweizeri* are two of the most threatened herpetofauna species in Greece, but at least twelve other species are under threat and in need of conservation. These are: *Mertensiella luschani, Bombina bombina, Testudo marginata, Chamaeleo chamaeleon, Lacerta danfordi, Mabuya aurata, Blanus strauchi, Eryx jaculus, Coluber nummifer, Eirenis modesta, Vipera xanthina* and *Vipera ursinii.*

There is widespread killing of all snake species but the major threat to Greece's amphibians and reptiles is the agricultural intensification of lowland habitats. This intensification is involving, amongst other activities, the widespread drainage and pollution of wetlands, especially coastal marshes. The widespread burning of forest, maquis and garrigue (especially on holiday islands) is a particular threat to island communities and endemic species. Some fires are accidental and related to hot summers and tourist influxes, but extensive deliberate burning also takes place for the purposes of creating new grazing areas from forest, improving grazing, land speculation for development, and so on. A recent law has returned previously state-owned land, including forest, to local communities and there has been a significant increase in forest clearance and destruction as a result. Locally, uncontrolled mining and quarrying poses a significant threat to key habitats for *Vipera schweizeri* on Milos.

Although illegal, collection for the pet trade and for souvenirs is essentially uncontrolled. Species at risk include *Testudo* spp.,

Chamaeleo chamaeleon, Eryx jaculus and *Vipera schweizeri*. Despite past arrests of reptile smugglers on Milos (involving the pre-arranged sale and export of the endangered *V. schweizeri* via visiting herpetologists) no prosecutions have been pursued and it is therefore likely that the practice of illegal collection and export continues unabated.

Rana ridibunda has been heavily and unsustainably exploited for export from northern Greece to France (in breach of the requirements of Appendix III of the Berne Convention). It is not clear whether this activity is continuing, or whether the decline from the 1981 high of 108 tons of live frogs to 36 tons by 1984 simply reflected a serious reduction in the resource.

Caretta caretta is under significant threat, particularly on Zakynthos which holds the largest nesting population in the Mediterranean. Many reports have been received of illegal and destructive activities at Laganas, deliberate killing of turtles and physical threats to researchers and conservationists, but none of these breaches of the law appear ever to have been pursued by local police or the courts.

Forestry and agriculture are a threat everywhere, but are particularly serious to key herpetofauna habitats in the Evros region (see Chapter 5).

Despite the identification of key herpetofauna sites, habitat destruction continues. One example was 150ha of Alyki Heath near Kitros, identified as a key herpetofauna site by Oxford University. Proposals for its conservation and subsequent refusal for development resulted in its immediate burning and ploughing with consequent heavy mortality of tortoises, large lizards and snakes. No legal actions or penalties were ever pursued, and this important site is again under threat.

Conservation Measures Taken

Approximately two-thirds of Greece's amphibians and reptiles are protected by law but there is no implementation of this law. The cases of illegal collection of *V. schweizeri* on Milos, damage to turtle nesting beaches at Laganas, and the deliberate destruction of Alyki Heath are three examples of the failure of the Greek authorities to implement laws to protect herpetofauna. Additionally there is no protection of habitats for herpetofauna other than some minimal and unenforced measures for part of the nesting habitat of *Caretta caretta* at Laganas Bay in Zakynthos.

Conservation Measures Needed

National laws should be amended to cover all Berne Convention Appendix II species and to protect the habitat of important sites for these species. Implementation of the Standing Committee of the Berne Convention Recommendations (see Appendices III and IV) for turtle nesting beaches and their marine surrounds (especially at Laganas), and for the critical habitats on western Milos and Evros is badly needed.

Appropriate protection should be afforded to areas of the Pindus mountains in order to protect relict populations of *Vipera ursinii* and *Lacerta agilis* (this unspoilt area still supports wolf and bear populations).

The key site of Alyki Heath should be properly protected.

Special measures should be taken for protecting the sites and habitat for vulnerable and rare species, including those with restricted distributions, but with particular priority to the endemic *Testudo marginata* for which the high density population at Gytheion should be protected.

Educational projects should be undertaken to promote an awareness of the conservation needs of the Greek herpetofauna, with particular emphasis on discouraging the killing of snakes.

Field survey and conservation assessments should be carried out for those areas known to hold important herpetofaunal assemblages in the Peloponnese and on Corfu.

All island populations of *Podarcis erhardii* should be assessed and classified according to their degree of speciation and isolation, and appropriate conservation measures taken to ensure the survival of representative genetic components of this taxa.

35
Turkey

Species Summary

Number of indigenous species: 121

Tailed amphibians:	7	*Mertensiella luschani, M. caucasica, Salamandra salamandra, Triturus vulgaris, T. cristatus, T. vittatus, Neurergus crocatus*
Tailless amphibians:	11	*Bufo bufo, B. viridis, Hyla arborea, H. savignyi, Rana camerani, R. dalmatina, R. holtzi, R. macrocnemis, R. ridibunda, Bombina bombina, Pelodytes caucasicus, Pelobates syriacus*
Tortoises and turtles:	8	*Caretta caretta, Chelonia mydas, Trionyx euphraticus, T. triunguis, Emys orbicularis, Mauremys caspica, Testudo graeca, T. hermanni*
Lizards:	53	*Cyrtopodion kotschyi, C. heterocercus, C. basoglui, Hemidactylus turcicus, Asaccus elisae, Ptyodactylus puiseuxi, Stenodactylus stenodactylus, Varanus griseus, Stellio caucasica, S. stellio, Trapelus ruderatus, Phrynocephalus helioscopus, Chamaeleo chamaeleon, Ophisaurus apodus, Anguis fragilis, L. cappadocica, L. danfordi, L. anatolica, L. oertzeni, L. laevis, L. uzzelli, L. raddei, L. parvula, L. mehelyi, L. parva, L. rudis, L. agilis, L. trilineata, L. strigata, L. pamphylica, L. valentini, L. armeniaca, L. unisexualis, L. media, L. princeps, L. viridis, L. clarkorum,*

		L. derjugini, Acanthodactylus boskianus, Eremias pleskei, Eremias strauchi, E. suphani, Ophisops elegans, Podarcis taurica, P. muralis, P. sicula, Ablepharus bivittatus, A. kitaibelii, Chalcides ocellatus, Eumeces schneideri, Mabuya aurata, M. vittata, Ophiomorus punctatissimus
Amphisbaenian:	1	*Blanus strauchi*
Snakes:	42	*Typhlops vermicularis, Leptotyphlops macrorhynchus, Eryx jaculus, Coluber caspius, C. jugularis, C. najadum, C. ravergieri, C. nummifer, C. rubriceps, C. ventromaculatus, Coronella austriaca, Elaphe quatuorlineata, E. longissima, E. persica, E. hohenackeri, E. situla, Malpolon monspessulanus, Natrix natrix, N. megalocephala, N. tessellata, Telescopus fallax, Eirenis eiselti, E. collaris, E. modesta, E. coronella, E. rothii, E. decemlineata, E. punctatolineata, E. lineomaculata, Pseudocyclophys persicus, Rhynchocalamus satunini, Spalerosophis diadema, Vipera wagneri, V. bulgardaghica, V. barani, V. ursinii, V. kaznakovi, V. ammodytes, V. xanthina, V. raddei, V. lebetina, V. renardi*

State of Knowledge

With the exception of some surveys of marine turtle beaches, no national surveys or status assessments are known to have been carried out and there are no published distribution maps. Some detailed work has been carried out by foreign herpetologists on the rarer species, particularly for vipers.

Turkey is a large country having zoogeographical influences and zoogeographical connections with the Middle East and the Caucasus (rich in herpetofauna species). Apart from the number of endemic species and subspecies there are also species whose distribution reach their westernmost limits in Turkey. Turkey boasts some 40 per cent of the total herpetofauna covered in this book and being a comparatively under-developed country there is enormous potential for assessing its wildlife resource and making proper plans for its conservation before the environmental disasters illustrated by the more developed countries take place.

Species Threats

Two species, *Chelonia mydas* (see Chapter 4) and *Vipera kaznakovi* are critically endangered. The latter species now has around 90 per cent of its world population concentrated in the 10 per cent of its range that lies within Turkey. Here, and in the Soviet Union, tourism and associated development of the eastern Black Sea coast has been the main cause of decline. This localised population is now seriously endangered from foreign snake collectors and one Turkish trader. Villages collect every specimen they can find so that they may sell to these collectors and many snakes die during this process.

The endemic *Vipera bulgardaghica* may be extinct - no specimens have been reported this century. However, its Cilician Taurus range may not have been comprehensively surveyed and localised populations might still occur.

Another endemic viper, *Vipera wagneri*, has recently been confirmed from two small localities in the north-east, and these sites have been kept confidential to avert threats from collection.

A further restricted species *Vipera raddei* may be locally abundant but some populations have been more or less exterminated by Swiss snake dealers in recent years.

The endemic *Rana holtzi* has its entire world range confined to two very small lakes and, although it is presently abundant there, it must be considered as vulnerable to threats of habitat change, pollution and the introduction of predatory fish.

Four other species are endemic, with restricted ranges, and may be vulnerable now or in the future. These are *Neurergus crocatus*, *Eremias suphani*, *Lacerta uzzelli* and the recently described *Vipera barani* whose field status is not yet well known.

Three other turtles are of conservation concern: *Caretta caretta*, whose Turkish nesting beaches support the largest breeding population left in the Mediterranean, and the large freshwater turtles *Trionyx euphraticus* and *T. triunguis*, both which are persecuted by fishermen and whose specialised egg-laying habitats put the species at risk.

Rhynchocalamus satunini and *Coluber rubriceps* have a restricted range in Turkey and are not abundant elsewhere, as to a lesser extent are *Mertensiella luschani* and *M. caucasica, Bombina bombina, Rana dalmatina, Ablepharus bivittatus* and *Vipera ursinii.*

Species with restricted ranges in Turkey but at the edge of their distribution are those from the north-east, near the borders of the Soviet Union and Iran, and from the south-east, respectively: *Pelodytes caucasicus, Eremias pleskei, E. strauchi, Lacerta clarkorum, L. derjugini, L. agilis brevicaudata*; and *Asaccus elisae, Ptyodactylus puiseuxi, Stenodactylus stenodactylus, Varanus griseus* (potentially at risk from hunting and persecution), *Acanthodactylus boskianus, Lacerta laevis, Lacerta princeps kurdistanica, Leptotyphlops macrorhynchus, Coluber ventromaculatus, Eirenis decemlineata, E. punctatolineata, E. rothii, Spalerosophis diadema.*

The large-scale commercial collection and export of tortoises has declined but still continues and its effect on wild populations is not monitored. The potential impact of collection on the already localised *Testudo hermanni* and on local populations of *T. graeca* is of concern.

Conservation Measures Taken

With the exception of the two marine turtles, none of the Turkish herpetofauna is protected by law. Turtle protection is inadequate and without local implementation or necessary public education. While nesting beaches and marine habitats for turtles are not protected by law, the important beaches of North Calis and Dalyan were protected in 1988 under the provisions of the Barcelona Convention, and a large tourism development halted at Dalyan in favour of turtle conservation. No other protected areas or National Parks are known to have been designated for herpetofauna in part or whole, although *Vipera ursinii anatolica* has its known range within the forest reserve of Ciglikara Ormani.

Conservation Measures Needed

Species protection law is urgently needed to bring national law in line with the Berne Convention, which Turkey has ratified. Additionally, other threatened species not yet listed in Appendix II of the

Convention, require protecting. In particular, the collection of and trade in tortoises requires urgent action.

Urgent measures to protect habitat for *Chelonia mydas* and to enhance hatching rates must be taken at the five remaining breeding localities for this turtle (see Chapter 4 for more details), and for *Caretta caretta* as recommended by the Standing Committee of the Berne Convention (Appendices III and V).

The main locality for *Vipera kaznakovi* must be protected, further collection prohibited and consideration given to the production of a species recovery plan.

Nature reserves should be designated to protect the habitat of *Vipera wagneri* and *V. raddei*, and action taken to prevent collection of both species.

Sites must be adequately protected to conserve the populations of the endemic and scientifically important *Lacerta uzzelli*.

Breeding sites for *Trionyx euphraticus* and *Trionyx triunguis* should be identified and protected, and current persecution stopped.

Conservation measures must be enacted to protect the world range of *Rana holtzi* (only a few hectares) and similar measures could have benefit for *Vipera bulgardaghica* whose last sighting was in this area.

Critical habitat around Lake Van for *Neurergus crocatus, Eremias suphani* and *Ablepharus bivittatus* should be protected.

Given suitable survey and habitat assessments, there is much scope for the identification of critical habitats and species assemblages for which reserves should be created. The following are the priority areas for such surveys:

- The Adana region (particularly for *Lacerta laevis, Coluber rubriceps, Eirenis decemlineata, Eirenis punctatolineata, Eirenis rothii* and *Rhynchocalamus satunini*).
- Parts of the Turkish/Soviet Union border.
- Parts of the Turkish/Syria border.

36
Cyprus

Species Summary

Number of indigenous species: 27-32

Tailed amphibians:	1	*Triturus vittatus*
Tailless amphibians:	3-4	*(Bufo bufo), Bufo viridis, Hyla savignyi, Rana ridibunda*
Tortoises and turtles:	3	*Mauremys caspica, Chelonia mydas, Caretta caretta*
Lizards:	11-12	*Hemidactylus turcicus, Cyrtopodion kotschyi, Stellio stellio, Chamaeleo chamaeleon, Ophisops elegans, Acanthodactylus schreib- eri, Lacerta laevis, Ablepharus kitaibelii, Chalcides ocellatus, Mabuya vittata, (M. aurata), Eumeces schneideri*
Amphisbaenians:	1	*Blanus strauchi*
Snakes:	8-11	*Typhlops vermicularis, Malpolon monspes- sulanus, Coluber najadum, C. jugularis, C. cypriensis, C. nummifer, (Natrix natrix, N. tessellata, Eirenis modesta), Telescopus fallax, Vipera lebetina*

State of Knowledge

No regional or national surveys have been undertaken and no mapping data exist. The available information is therefore limited chiefly to data collected by visiting foreign herpetologists, usually as

259

brief reports and museum specimens. Past nesting beaches (mainly in the south and west) for marine turtles have been identified by the Ministry of Fisheries. In 1988, WWF funded a survey of current nesting beaches in the north and east. Apart from this work on the turtles, the distributions of other species have not yet been investigated and the current status of most species is not known, hence the unresolved queries over the actual occurrence of five species.

Species Threats

Three species are considered endangered: *Chelonia mydas, Caretta caretta,* and the endemic snake *Coluber cypriensis.* In addition, many species reliant on aquatic habitats appear to have declined and are now rare or vulnerable because of pollution and the loss of freshwater habitats. These threatened species include *Triturus vittatus, Hyla savignyi, Bufo viridis, Mauremys caspica* and *Natrix natrix* (probably extinct).

Snake persecution is widespread and probably based on fears about the poisonous *Vipera lebetina.* Persecution is thought to have caused local, regional and possibly national declines of this and other species. Drivers are frequently observed to stop their vehicles, reverse and then run over any observed snake, even those already crushed previously! The larger lizards also suffer from persecution. Folk-lore claims that *Chamaeleo chamaeleon* is an avid biter of noses and *Stellio stellio* of testicles!

Traditionally farmed terraced fields and their associated stone walls provide good reptile habitats, but recent and continuing agricultural intensification of lowlands in the south and west, as well as urban development, is having adverse consequences. Additionally, increasingly intensive forestry management is degrading natural and semi-natural forests and their associated habitats in the Troodas mountains, while the important biological areas of the Akamas peninsula are threatened by uncontrolled tourism development.

Conservation Measures Taken

Very little active conservation is carried out. An exception is the protection of North Lara beach under forestry law for nesting turtles and its hatchery programme for the turtles. Draft legislation is currently in Parliament which is aimed at protecting the private beaches of South Lara and Toxeftra. The Cypriot authorities in the north-east are now pledged to conserve turtle nesting sites.

Although Cyprus has recently ratified the Berne Convention, there is as yet no legislation to protect reptiles and amphibians or their habitats, with the exception of *Chelonia mydas* and *Caretta caretta*, and more recently, *Mauremys caspica*.

Conservation Measures Needed

Legislation is required in order to bring Cypriot law in line with the obligations of the Berne Convention. Eight other species (including *Coluber cypriensis*) are not even listed by the Berne Convention. Several other noted and endemic subspecies including *Cyrtopodion kotschyi fitzingeri, Stellio stellio cyprica, Chamaeleo chamaeleon rectiscristata, Eumeces schneideri schneideri, Acanthodactylus schreiberi schreiberi, Ophisops elegans schluteri, Lacerta laevis troodica, Telescopus fallax cyprianus* and *Vipera lebetina lebetina* also require conservation. It would not be surprising if some of these endemics were subsequently upgraded to species level to separate them from those occurring on the European/Asian mainland.

All surviving turtle-nesting beaches require protection and active conservation, with an immediate priority for those beaches which still support *Chelonia mydas*.

Field surveys should be undertaken to identify critical habitats and site protection options for *Coluber cypriensis*.

Herpetofaunal surveys should be undertaken for the Akamas peninsula and the Troodas mountains, and the designation of nature reserves pursued.

Public education programmes are badly needed in order to deter people from the national pastime of snake-killing.

Appendix I

**Recommendation 13 (1988) of the Standing Committee
of the Convention on the Conservation of European
Wildlife and Natural Habitats (Berne Convention)
Concerning Measures for the Protection of Critical
Biotopes of Endangered Amphibians and Reptiles**

The Standing Committee of the Convention on the Conservation of European Wildlife and Natural Habitats, acting under the terms of Article 14 of the Convention;

Having regard to the aims of the Convention to conserve wild flora and fauna and their natural habitats;

Having regard to Resolution (78) 22 of the Committee of Ministers of the Council of Europe on threatened amphibians and reptiles;

Having regard to Recommendations No. 7, 8 and 9 (1987) of the Standing Committee concerning the protection of marine turtles and their habitat;

Recalling that Article 3 provides that each Contracting Party shall take the necessary steps to promote national policies for the conservation of wild flora; wild fauna and natural habitats, with particular attention to endangered and vulnerable species, especially endemic ones, and endangered habitats;

Recalling that Article 4, paragraph 1, provides that each Contracting Party shall take appropriate and necessary legislative and administrative measures to ensure the conservation of the habitats of the wild flora and fauna species, especially those specified in Appendices I and II, and the conservation of endangered natural habitats;

Referring to the report of the European Herpetological Society on critical biotopes for endangered amphibians and reptiles;

A   RECOMMENDS THAT RELEVANT CONTRACTING PARTIES take the following urgent measures:

1.   Ensure appropriate management of meadows at Moosbrunn and Neudegg (Austria) by reducing mowing to one cut in the late autumn and survey these areas and the western part of Zitzmannsdorfer Wiesen (Austria) so that these critical biotopes for *Vipera ursinii rakosiensis* may maintain the species;

2   Pursue as far as possible the appropriate protection of the critical habitat of *Vipera lebetina* in West Milos (Greece), and strengthen controls against collection for trade of this species and of *Podarcis milensis*;

3   Pursue the appropriate protection of critical wooded areas in Evros (Greece), *inter alia* by examining the impact of the development activities undertaken in the area;

4   Manage the biogenetic reserve of Bosco della Fontana (Italy) to include annual pumping of water into the woodland, together with the provision or pools, so as to conserve this most important *Rana latastei* breeding population and to reverse its present decline at this unique site;

5   Enforce protection measures in critical areas of the Gulf of Orosei (Italy), taking into consideration the fact that this important biotope is severely threatened unless present projects of touristic development and new harbour constructions near Caletta di Osalla and Orosei are stopped; the new access tracks closed; and hunting, grazing, and wood exploitation adequately regulated, so as to permit the survival of the exceptionally high number of 19 species of amphibians and reptiles recorded in this area.

B.   RECOMMENDS MOREOVER THAT RELEVANT CONTRACTING PARTIES undertake the following actions:

1   Give, by use of the legal instruments of regional authorities in habitat protection, adequate protection to sites in Friuli-

Venezia Giulia (Italy) containing *Proteus anguinus*, by declaring the relevant caves as reserves and ensuring the integrity of their water systems;

2   Protect the most important sites for *Bombina bombina* at Storebaelt, southern Sjaelland and the archipelago south of Fyon (Denmark) and in Pevestorfer Elvwiesen (Federal Republic of Germany);

3   Ensure, by the most appropriate means, protection of the habitat of *Alytes muletensis* in Sierra de Tramuntana in Mallorca (Spain), and ensure the integrity of the water catchment area of the mountain streams in which this endangered species lives;

4   Extend the protection of Parco del Ticino (Italy) to include adjacent breeding sites of *Pelobates fuscus insubricus*;

5   Designate the protected area of Le Bine (Italy) as a biogenetic reserve and extend it to include the critical biotope of the largest surviving population of the threatened species *Rana latastei*;

6   Ensure, by the most appropriate means, protection of the habitat of *Podarcis hispanica atrata* in the Columbretes islands (Spain);

7   Ensure, by the most appropriate means, protection of the habitat of the rare or endangered populations of *Podarcis lilfordi* subspecies in the Cabrera archipelago, the small islands of Aire and Colomar and those close to Minorca and Mallorca (Spain);

8   Ensure, by the most appropriate means, protection of the different habitats of threatened subspecies of *Podarcis pityusensis* in the small islands of Bledas, Espartas, Vedras, Margaalida, Es Freus, Murada, Conillera and Cana (offshore of Ibiza and Formentera) (Spain);

9   Continue the captive breeding programme of *Gallotia simonyi* in Hierro (Spain); ensure protection by the most appropriate means, of its only known habitat by preventing the grazing of goats and predation by cats; and consider the possibility of this species being reintroduced in other properly managed areas;

10   Safeguard the habitat of *Vipera ursinii ursinii* in relevant parts

of Gran Sasso (Italy) by adequate measures against recreation pressures, and control grazing so that Juniper is protected;

C   CALLS THE ATTENTION OF FRANCE TO THE NEED FOR ENSURING,

1   by the most appropriate means, protection of the biotopes of the most outstanding populations of *Vipera ursinii ursinii* in France.

Appendix II

**Resolution 22 (1978) of the Committee of Ministers
of the Council of Europe on Threatened
Amphibians and Reptiles in Europe**

The Committee of Ministers

(*omissis*)

Noting that because of the changes in habitats and their growing
scarcity on the one hand and the misuse of toxic substances on the
other, certain species of amphibians and reptiles have already
become extinct in Europe, at least fifty-nine are threatened (endangered, vulnerable, rare) and yet others may become so if the decline
in numbers continues;

(*omissis*)

Recommends that the governments of the Council of Europe
member states be guided in their environmental policies by the
following principles:

General Principles

1.   Adequate protection for all amphibians and reptiles with the
       exception of exotic species;

2.   Special attention to species threatened or liable to become
       so, until their numbers have again reached a satisfactory
       level;

Monitoring, Inventory and Research

3.   Setting up where necessary a national body to keep watch on
       threatened faunal species;

4.   Preparing or updating of a national list of threatened am-

phibians and reptiles drawing attention, in particular, to the reasons for the decline of these species and presenting the measures required to guarantee their survival;

5. Ensure that there are appropriate co-ordinated programmes of herpetological research in order to gain a better knowledge of the ecological requirements of these species and to encourage the allocation of the necessary funds to the competent bodies;

Protection and Management of Habitats

6. Conservation and protection of existing habitats, their reconstitution or, where necessary, creation of new ones. These should be sufficiently large to satisfy the ecological needs of the species and include a variety of biotopes so that they may be colonised by many groups of species;

7. Setting up of protected areas in the Mediterranean region in those parts of the coast where turtles breed;

8. Measures to facilitate the reproduction and seasonal migration of amphibians and reptiles;

9. Selection from among protected areas of habitats, biocenoses and ecosystems sheltering threatened amphibian and reptile species with a view to applying for their inclusion in the European network of biogenetic reserves;

10. Management of protected areas according to ecological principles and allocation of the funds required for the purpose;

Specific Dispostions

11. Control human activity and particularly the use of toxic substances which could prove harmful to amphibians and reptiles and their habitats;

12. Control strictly and where necessary prohibit the introduction of non-indigenous species liable to compete with amphibians and reptiles and thus reduce their numbers, especially in island or isolated habitats where the biological balance is easily disturbed;

13. Abolition of the bonus system in force for the destruction of

reptiles considered as harmful, including venomous ones;

14.   Severe restriction of the capture of wild amphibians and reptiles for the pet trade and other commercial purposes or for the production of serums and the replacement of this practice by the raising of species in captivity or semi-liberty, in controlled environments similar to the natural ones, for instance with a view to:

(i)   collecting snake venom and preparing lyophilised serums;

(ii)   providing research laboratories with amphibians and reptiles solely when the use of these species cannot be replaced by other methods;

International Co-operation

15.   Consideration of the possibility of ratifying, where they have not already done so, the Convention on International Trade in Endangered Species of Wild Fauna and Flora concluded in Washington on 3 March 1973;

Information of the Public

16.   Encourage and promote public information and teaching in primary and secondary schools concerning:

(i)   the place of amphibians and reptiles in the biological balance of nature;

(ii)   the need to protect amphibians and reptiles (especially the venomous ones), among others by the wide circulation of the study on threatened amphibians and reptiles in Europe.

Appendix III

**Recommendation 7 (1987) of the Standing Committee
of the Convention on the Conservation of European
Wildlife and Natural Habitats (Berne Convention)
Concerning the Protection of Marine Turtles
and Their Habitat**

The Standing Committee of the Convention on the Conservation of European Wildlife and Natural Habitats, acing under the terms of Article 14 of the Convention;

(*omissis*)

Considering that marine turtles present in the Mediterranean are seriously endangered as a result of deterioration of their nesting beaches by tourism, direct killing, accidents in fishing nets and capture in long-line fishing, having experienced a drastic reduction in their number in the last year;

RECOMMENDS THAT THE RELEVANT PARTIES embark without delay on the following work:

1. Give adequate legal protection or as appropriate assistance for protection to the main nesting beaches of marine turtles and enforce conservation measures wherever existing, in particular in Zakynthos (Greece); Dalyan, Ayatan and Yumurtalik (Turkey); and Lara, Toxeftra, Polis and Latsi (Cyprus);

2. Avoid any new touristic or other development in important nesting areas. If not possible, any new development should be subject to an environmental impact assessment carried out from the start in collaboration with all interested groups (scientists, local authorities, decision makers). Wherever

there are already constructions, strict regulations should be applied so as to respect the ecological needs of sea turtles;

3.   Promote a coordinated research programme on marine turtles, setting the following themes as priorities:

- mapping of nesting densities,
- location of feeding and wintering areas and migratory routes,
- effects of different forms of fishing and pollution on turtle populations,
- biological studies on artificial hatcheries so that this solution may be used if needed;

4.   Intensify cooperation between all States directly concerned and, in collaboration with the relevant scientific societies and international organisations (EEC, UNEP, IUCN) provide appropriate means (financial and other) to achieve efficiency;

5.   Promote information campaigns addressed to the general public and relevant target groups (school children, fishermen, tour operators, tourists and local and regional authorities), especially in sensitive areas;

6.   Enforce present regulations concerning commercialising marine turtles and their derivatives.

Appendix IV

**Recommendation 9 (1987) of the Standing Committee
of the Convention on the Conservation of European
Wildlife and Natural Habitats (Berne Convention)
Concerning the Protection of *Caretta caretta*
in Laganas Bay, Zakynthos (Greece)**

The Standing Committee of the Convention on the Conservation of
European Wildlife and Natural Habitats, acting under the terms of
Article 14 of the Convention;

(*omissis*)

Considering that the loggerhead turtle *Caretta caretta* is seriously
endangered mainly as a result of habitat loss in its nesting grounds,
which suffer important deterioration as a result of touristic activities;

Recognising the capital importance of Laganas Bay beaches for the
survival of *Caretta caretta* as they hold the highest known concentration of nests of this species in the whole of the Mediterranean basin;

(*omissis*)

Recognising the efforts of the Government of Greece to control
touristic development in the area and its will to preserve the quality
of Laganas Bay for successful *Caretta caretta* breeding;

Recognising the need for the adequate enforcement of the Presidential decrees and Ministerial decisions regulating human activities in Zakynthos;

RECOMMENDS that the Government of Greece embark without
delay on the following actions:

1. Remove the prefabricated houses in Dafni;

2. Remove walls and concrete platforms built in the optimal sites for turtle nesting at Kalamaki and eastern Laganas beaches unless these are supporting the soil of existing dwelling houses;

3. As a matter of priority, acquire the 100 metres band closest to the beach limit, wherever this land is not developed, in Kalamaki and eastern Laganas and a bank of appropriate land within Sekania and Dafni;

4. Set the legal limits of the public land on all beaches at Laganas Bay;

5. Remove trees and ban and penalise the use of deck-chairs, sunshades and pedaloes on the nesting beaches of Gerakas, Kalamaki, eastern Laganas and Marathonisi;

6. Close the access of vehicles to the beaches from all roads and effectively enforce this ban;

7. Replace existing lights shining on the beaches or reorientate them in such a way that their impact on turtles is minimised;

8. Assess the potential of Laganas Bay (except western Laganas beach) to qualify for a stricter protection category, such as a marine park, natural park, natural monument or other appropriate legal term;

9. Reassess the potential impact of the development of the village of Kalamaki and neighbouring areas on sea turtle nesting.

Appendix V

**Recommendation 8 (1987) of the Standing Committee
of the Convention on the Conservation of European
Wildlife and Natural Habitats (Berne Convention)
Concerning the Protection of Marine Turtles in
Dalyan and Other Important Areas in Turkey**

The Standing Committee of the Convention on the Conservation of
European Wildlife and Natural Habitats, acting under the terms of
Article 14 of the Convention;

(*omissis*)

Considering that marine turtles nesting on Mediterranean beaches,
such as *Caretta caretta* and *Chelonia mydas*, are seriously endangered mainly as a result of habitat loss in their nesting grounds,
which suffer important deterioration from touristic developments
and other human activities;

Recognising the great importance of Dalyan as a nesting beach for
Caretta caretta and *Chelonia mydas*;

(*omissis*)

RECOMMENDS that the Government of Turkey:

1.   Consider the protection of the Dalyan area as a national park
       or a biogenetic reserve in order to ensure the protection of
       sea turtles and Mediterranean monk seals as priorities;

2.   Avoid any new touristic development in the Dalyan area;

3.   Consider the protection of the beaches and marine surround-
       ings of Akyatan and Yumurtalik;

4.   Reassess present land use plans for the south and south-west

coasts of the country, taking into consideration the preservation of valuable coastal areas, including the main nesting beaches of sea turtles.